The Righteous Rage *of a* Ten-Year-Old Boy

A JOURNEY OF SELF-DISCOVERY

WRITTEN BY

JUSTIN B. LONG

Nonfiction books by Justin B. Long

Adventures of the Horse Doctor's Husband
More Adventures of the Horse Doctor's Husband
How to Become an Equine Veterinarian – coauthored with Erica Lacher, DVM
The Righteous Rage of a Ten-Year-Old Boy

Fiction books by J. Boyd Long

Genesis Dimension – *The DimWorld Series* Book 1
When Good Plans Go Bad - *The DimWorld Series* Book 2
Inside the Machine - *The DimWorld Series* Book 3

This book is memoir. It reflects the author's present recollections of experiences over time. Some names and characteristics have been changed, some events have been compressed, and some dialogue has been recreated. Although the author has made every effort to ensure that the information in this book was correct at press time, the author does not assume and hereby disclaims any liability to any party for any loss, damage, or disruption caused by errors or omissions, whether such errors or omissions result from negligence, accident, or any other cause.

Published in the United States by Mad Goat Press LLC

Gainesville, Florida USA

MadGoatPress.com

Cover design by My Custom Book Cover

ISBN 978-1-948169-53-0 Ebook

ISBN 978-1-948169-54-7 Paperback

ISBN 978-1-948169-55-4 Hardcover

Library of Congress Control Number: 2020922502

For more information, please email the publisher at
info@MadGoatPress.com

Author website: JBoydLong.com

For Amanda, who helped me find my truth

Author's Note

While this book contains descriptions of counseling sessions, it should be noted that many elements of those sessions have been omitted. The purpose of this book is not to depict the specific steps of therapy, but rather to give hope to those who suffer. I have taken liberties with my relating of these accounts to streamline the process. This is not a textbook on therapy, nor is it a do-it-yourself guidebook. This is a social proof that if you are committed to changing your life, and willing to accept help, you can learn to feel better about yourself. Any mistakes in the representation of therapy as a whole, or of the therapist involved, are mistakes in my memory of the events or in my retelling of them, and not the fault of anyone other than the author. While I'm far better than I've ever been as a result of therapy and sobriety, I'm still not perfect. Yet!

—Justin

Contents

Chapter 1

Erica and I sat at the kitchen table discussing the day ahead. After five years together, our morning routine was well-established: exercise, bring the horses in from the pastures and feed them, feed the donkeys and sheep, then the cats and dogs, then make breakfast for us.

"What are you doing today?" she asked between a bite of oatmeal and a swallow of coffee.

I glanced at my list. "I have to finish editing the leg bandaging video. I'm signing us up with a new drug distributor after that, and then I'm interviewing a couple of people for the tech position this afternoon."

"Any good candidates?"

I nodded over my coffee cup. "One, for sure. The other one has potential."

Hiring for our veterinary clinic was something that I had taken on with enthusiasm. It was one of many elements of running a small business that I knew nothing about when I met Erica but had immersed myself in learning. While everything about my position as the CFO of our vet practice, from bookkeeping to team building, had been baptism by fire, I understood early on what I *didn't* want the workplace to be. Nearly every employer on my eclectic resume had been a toxic work environment in one way or another, sometimes due to my own behavior, as I was learning. Running our clinic was my opportunity to create something positive, and I took that very seriously.

"What's the new distributor about? Are we switching primaries, or is this just a supplemental?"

"Supplemental. Their pricing on a few things is too good to pass up, but not on everything. How's your schedule look today?"

She snorted. "I've got six horses on the schedule, one of which is a lameness exam, and I've got another one texting me right now with a shoulder laceration. I'll be lucky to get home by eight o'clock tonight."

"Don't worry. Once we have a third vet, your schedule will loosen up."

We laughed together at the often-used joke. We'd been a three-vet practice for nearly two years, and she still didn't have any more time than before. The late nights prevented her from riding her horses as often as she wanted to, and I knew that bothered her a lot. What I didn't know was how to fix it, or if I should even try. Being busy was a good problem to have, at least from my perspective as the person paying the bills and managing the money.

Once Erica was off to work, I rinsed the breakfast dishes and walked over to my desk. Working from home was yet another wonderful aspect of my job and marriage, even with my mother-in-law living with us. While Erica spent her days practicing medicine on horses, I spent mine doing the bookkeeping and managing the business side of the practice. I also took care of our small Florida farm, which was home to horses, donkeys, and sheep, as well as cats and dogs. For an introvert like me, it was perfect. And I should have been happy. But I wasn't.

Maybe that's not quite right. I loved nearly everything about my life. I got to design my own job and be my own boss. Erica was my soulmate, the partner I'd never dreamed I'd find. Our marriage was healthy, strong, and wonderful. I was learning tons of new things about personal development, becoming a better leader, managing a business, and expanding my horizons. Erica and I had started a successful podcast about horse healthcare. We made videos for the clinic's YouTube channel. I was writing books, and some of them were doing really well. On a scale of one to ten, I would rate my life before Erica, whom I met when I was thirty-eight, at a four. My life after meeting Erica was a solid ten, no question. But sometimes things made me angry, which always turned into a negative funk, and once I started down that path, it was hard to get back out of it. I called it *The Pit of Despair*, a reference to one of my favorite movies, *The Princess Bride*.

As I worked my way through the online form for the distribution company, answering all kinds of questions about our business and finances, that familiar feeling crept over me. The more they pried into our business, the more indignant I became, until I was ready to attack them, to shout and stomp and tell them it was none of their business. This wasn't a new experience for me. It happened every time I had to deal with a big company. I knew going in that I was going to be angry before it was over.

Why? Why did I feel so persecuted? I felt like they were asking all these questions with the assumption that we weren't good enough to buy their products, or that our business wasn't being run well enough to meet their standards. It made me defensive, which always manifests as aggression. By the time I completed the form, I hated the distribution company as passionately as I was capable of. Before this new distributor, I wanted to go to war against the company that prints my books. Before them, it was AT&T. And if I've learned anything, it's that when it seems like it's everyone else, it's really me.

I started my journey into recovery from alcoholism in 2008. That led me to a lifestyle of self-discovery and self-awareness, which I fully committed myself to. So, when this anger-turned-depression thing became a pattern, I recognized it, and I didn't like what I saw. The way I felt about myself after one of these events was almost as bad as if I'd had a relapse with drinking. I was ashamed of the way my insecurities were driving my behavior. Something had to change.

Several years before I met Erica, I spent some time seeing a therapist. She helped me identify the new Justin— the one who was sober and trying to change his behavior— and separate him from the old Justin. That was a critical period in my life, and it taught me the value of asking for help.

Because of that experience, I knew it was time for me to get some counseling again. I did a Google search for therapists in my area and found one with a website that I liked. I made an appointment that same day before I could change my mind and procrastinate, and I immediately felt better. There is no satisfaction like knowing you're doing something to make your life better. I couldn't wait to talk to Erica about it when she got home that night.

After supper, we all went down to the barn. Erica brought a horse in from the pasture and began grooming it, while I absently played with the dog. We chatted for a bit, and once her mom went back across the driveway to her house, I spoke up.

"I made an appointment with a therapist."

Erica stood up on her tippy toes and peered at me over the back of the horse between us. "Really?"

I nodded.

She brushed the horse in silence for a moment, then came around to stand in front of me. The concern on her face startled me.

"What's wrong?" She turned and began slowly brushing the horse but kept her eyes on me.

Erica has supported me a thousand percent on everything I've wanted to do. When I started a side business building websites, she referred new clients to me. When I wanted to form my own publishing company, she helped me prioritize my schedule and delegate things to create space. When I decided to start producing videos for our veterinary clinic and podcast patrons, she committed her time to make it happen. She believed in me long before I believed in myself in terms of my ability to become a good business owner, and I knew she would support me on this, too.

"I keep getting sucked into the pit of despair, and I'm tired of it. I don't know if I have a rage problem, or what's going on, but if I'm going to run the clinic, I can't be losing my mind every time I have to deal with a vendor. That's not who I want to be."

"Should I be doing something?" She stopped brushing for a moment. "Do you need something from me that I'm not giving you?"

I burst out laughing. "What? No, this isn't about us, not even remotely. This is about me needing more tools for emotional management. You're a natural leader with impeccable self-control, but I'm the opposite of that. I need to learn how to be composed and calm and quit taking everything personally."

She smiled, but the lines around her eyes remained. "Okay. But whatever we need to do to make things okay for you, we'll do it. I just need you to tell me, okay?"

I put my arms around her and drew her tight against my chest. "Don't worry. Therapy is a wonderful thing. I have a feeling I'm about to go on another big growth spurt, and I'm excited about it."

Erica had a great upbringing, and she launched into the world emotionally healthy and self-confident. We often discussed how different our childhoods were and how clearly that had impacted our lives. The idea of going to therapy is something she'd never needed to consider, and I don't think she knew what to think about my decision. Her concern made me feel loved, but I didn't want her to worry about me.

"This will be good, I promise. Think of it as self-improvement coaching. I'm going to learn how to improve my emotional intelligence." I stepped back with a grin. "But right now, I'm going to put the sheep out back with the donkeys for the night and then take a shower. Don't stay up playing with your horse too late."

As I drifted off to sleep that night, I spent a minute reveling in the thrill of embarking on a new adventure. My life had started off rough, but for the last twelve years, I'd been on a mission to make it better. I'd felt this thrill enough times before to know that it would be followed by growth, and while that involved pain at times, it always ended with me being in a better place than where I started.

This round of therapy was the next chapter of my life, and I had a feeling it was going to be a big one. And I was right.

Chapter 2

I SAT IN THE BLACK LEATHER CHAIR in my therapist's office, trembling with anger and indignation. My lizard brain just wanted to smash things, to burn off my feelings with mindless violence. While I rarely gave in, I wanted to learn how to grow past such urges and stop living as a victim of my emotions. It was my third session, and we were starting to work on specific things. It was good, but it was painful, too.

Our first couple of sessions had been spent getting to know one another and doing some preliminary groundwork. We talked about what I wanted to work on, and made a list of topics to go over in the coming year. She also had me come up with a list of fictional characters who would be my support team. Not being the superhero type, I picked Bob Ross as my first team member. Watching his painting show from the eighties was one of my favorite ways to unwind. His unflappable calmness was the opposite of my flash temper, so he was an easy choice.

"I want you to really get inside of that feeling," Nysa was saying. "Move past the mindless rage and find the core of it. Yes, you're mad at AT&T on the surface, but what's beneath the anger?"

We were talking about triggering events. I was well-acquainted with the concept that underlying insecurities drove my emotional response to certain things, and that most of my problems stemmed from negative beliefs about myself. Knowing it was one thing. Doing something about it was another.

Getting to the bottom of the rage was tough. I thought about all the things that had gone wrong with the internet installation project at our veterinary clinic, and how AT&T had handled it, or more appropriately, *not* handled it. For example, no one had told me that as the business owner, I needed to have a ground wire installed to the hardware rack for the box they were putting in. When the installation team showed up, they had to reschedule because I didn't have that done. Then they charged me three hundred fifty dollars for rescheduling. That's how it went for the entire three months it took to get the internet up and running.

"I think I just feel helpless," I said. "They're screwing me over, and I can't do anything about it. That's what pisses me off."

Nysa shifted in her chair. "*Helpless.* That's a good word. Let's explore it. Do you feel this way about other things you can't control?"

One of the many things I've learned about myself is that I'm a control freak. I'm not a micro-manager, and I've used that to convince myself that I'm *not* a control freak. But when I defend myself by saying things like, *I allow my team members to decide the best way to do things*, I am still presenting myself as being in ultimate control. I'm *allowing* them to make a decision.

"It's not an across-the-board reaction to things. I mean, I certainly don't like it when I get cut out of the decision-making process at work, which happens sometimes, but that's not the same as this. That's me feeling left out or unimportant, and this is me feeling like I'm the victim of an injustice."

"Now we're getting somewhere." Nysa jotted down some notes. "*Victim of an injustice.* Let's go with that. Give me another example of that happening."

Several things came to mind. Getting caught up in a battle between a company I once worked for and the labor union that got voted in, which resulted in me losing my job. Being demoted in the Army for a minor infraction. Reaching back to the heart of the matter, my childhood, I found more.

"Here's one. When I was in high school, I saved up money and bought my first car. I didn't borrow any money from my parents, not that they had any. I worked, I saved up, and I paid cash for this old 1976 Chevy Blazer. It was mine, and my dad grounded me from it. I don't even remember what crime I committed against him, but I remember the war over whether he had the power to take my keys. He won, because he always won, but I remember that helpless rage. I hated that feeling. Still do."

"Okay, that's a good example," Nysa said. "Give me another one."

The memory that surfaced was old, but the jagged edges were still sharp. "My dad came home from work one day and went out to the garage to do something. I was in my room doing a school assignment. I think I was in third or fourth grade. Anyway, three seconds after he went outside, he was right back in the house screaming for me."

I closed my eyes, trying to conjure the old terror I used to feel at the sound of my name. It came back surprisingly easily, the recipe having been used so many times: two parts urge to run, one part gut cramp like I need to use the bathroom, and one part overwhelming desire to cease existing.

"Justin Boyd!" my dad shouted. He always used my first and middle names when he was mad. "Justin Boyd!"

I flew out of my room and met him at the back door. When he was enraged, speed was of the essence. My mind raced, trying to come up with a source for his ire. What could I have done? He hadn't even made it to the garage before whatever it was caught his attention. Had I forgotten a task he'd assigned me? Something in the back yard I was supposed to do?

He grabbed me by the ear, one of his favorite control points, and dragged me out the back door. I knew a beating was inevitable at this point, and tears of resignation began to form against my will.

"What the hell is this shit?" He shook his fist as he spoke, driving spikes of pain deep inside my skull.

The searing pain in my eardrum was making me dizzy, and I tried to move my head in time with his hand so he wouldn't tear my ear off. "I don't know what you mean!"

He switched his grip to the sides of my head and spun it roughly from left to right, forcing me to pan the back yard. "That!"

When my vision stabilized, I realized there was trash all over the ground. Literally everywhere. One of the dumpster carts lay on its side near the pecan tree. My first thought was that a stray dog had scattered the trash, but a dog couldn't have pulled the cart in from the alley where we kept it. It had to have been a person, probably one of the kids from school.

"Were you too lazy to take the trash out?" he demanded, shaking my head. "Did you think you could just throw it out in the yard and get away with it?"

It finally dawned on me that he thought I was responsible. "No, I didn't do that! Why would I?"

"Do you think I'm stupid? Who else would have done it?" He shoved me back in the house. "Go get the board."

He'd made the paddle himself, which he dubbed *The Board*, for the sole purpose of spanking me. Sending me to fetch my instrument of punishment was another of his favorite moves.

Arguing with him was useless. He believed that I'd thrown trash all over the yard, even though I'd never done anything like that in my life. Nothing I could say would change his mind because he was incapable of admitting that he was wrong. I ran to the cabinet where he kept the paddle and hurried back out with it. I wanted to scream right in his face that he was being stupid, that if he'd just think about it for ten seconds, he'd realize how ridiculous he was being. Instead, I handed him the paddle and silently accepted my fate.

"Get the trash can," he growled, snatching the board out of my hand. "We're going to pick this up, and you'll get one swat for every piece of trash in this yard. I promise you'll never pull a stunt like this again."

I was used to getting spanked, but never more than ten or fifteen licks. One swat for every piece of trash? He couldn't be serious, right? An icy spear of dread shot through me as he grabbed my other ear and dragged me to the first item, an empty mac and cheese box. As I dropped it in the cart, the board cracked across the back of my legs.

One.

I opened my eyes, coming back to the present.

Nysa stared at me. "Do you remember how many pieces of trash there were?"

"One hundred and four."

"You got a hundred and four swats?"

The memory, at least thirty-five years old, was still clear. Every detail all the way down to the way my legs burned. "Yeah. It took a while, but we got it all picked up."

She shook her head. "Did you ever find out how it really happened?"

"No." I looked down. "No, but I'm sure it was one of the kids in the neighborhood trying to stick it to my dad. He wasn't very popular. Or maybe they were trying to stick it to me, I don't know. I wasn't very popular, either."

"What did that event make you believe about yourself?"

It was easy to feel the rage, the overwhelming sense of injustice. I remembered pulling the can slowly from one piece of trash to the next, trying to buy an extra second or two of recovery time, my legs and butt on fire from my knees to my spine. Dreading the next swat, knowing it was going to land somewhere that already stung because there weren't any fresh places left after the first twenty strikes. Using the helpless anger as motivation to keep going in hopes that he would someday know that he'd been wrong about this and be consumed by his guilt. My feelings for my dad were easy to identify, but the ones about myself were more obscure.

"I think I felt defeated and utterly alone," I said at last. "I was helpless, but the fact that I was going to take a totally undeserved beating hurt even more. My dad didn't believe me. I'd done nothing wrong. I'd told the truth, and I was being destroyed for it. When I tried, I failed. When I did nothing, I still failed. The deck was stacked against me."

She wrote in silence for a moment. "Okay. Let's take this all the way back, as far as you can into your childhood. What's the earliest time you can remember being the victim of an injustice?"

My childhood was an unbroken line of injustices, at least to me. To say that my relationship with my parents was adversarial would be like saying that space is big. It's technically true, but a gross understatement.

My dad ruled me totally and completely. He was quick with criticism and quicker with the paddle. I got a spanking nearly every day of my life until I was thirteen. My mom had her own debilitating emotional challenges, which she was sure that God would fix if she just prayed fervently enough, found the right church, and got involved to the level that He noticed her. Sometimes she was my ally, and sometimes she sold me out to my dad. I never knew which way it would go.

"I always had a heavy workload," I said. The eggshell wall of my therapist's office was decorated with an abstract picture of a motorcycle, and I stared at the spokes on the front wheel as I tried to unearth the buried memories. "My dad was the kind of guy who always had fifteen projects going, a real do-it-yourselfer. I don't think he ever paid anyone to do anything in his whole life. I was in awe of him in some ways. He knew how to do everything. Electrical stuff, plumbing, carpentry, working on the car, he did everything himself, and I was his laborer, the go-fetch runner, and the flashlight holder."

I closed my eyes again and explored things that I hadn't thought about in years. Crushing cans with the sixteen-pound sledgehammer that I could barely lift. Digging ditches for the new water line my dad was installing. Splitting firewood with that same sledgehammer, pounding steel wedges into the logs, praying that I didn't break another handle and invoke even more rage. Pulling nails from recycled lumber. Watching my friends ride by on their bicycles while I worked.

"This probably isn't the earliest, but it's what's coming to mind," I said at last.

"That's okay," she said. "Just go with it."

I glanced at her. The tiny diamond-chip studs in her upper lip reflected the light from her computer monitor, drawing my eyes away from her dark, purple-streaked hair. She wore a white sleeveless blouse above her long, pleated skirt, exposing slender arms covered in tattoos. I might've looked like a typical straitlaced white guy with my button-down shirt and khaki trousers, but I totally identified with her look on the inside. It was a defiant reaction to whatever trauma she had endured, and I got it. She was my people.

"One of my jobs was splitting and stacking firewood. Dad cut it to length with a chainsaw, and I did the rest. He built this rack behind the house, two poles in the ground vertically, maybe fifteen feet apart, and six feet high. There was a wire that went across the top from one pole to the other to keep them from splaying out under the weight. My job was to keep that space full and neatly stacked with firewood from one pole to the other, all the way up to the wire. There couldn't be any gaps at the top or any pieces out of line. We would stand at one end of it and count how many pieces were sticking out the front or the back, and then I would get a spanking, one swat for each piece. The injustice for me was that the wood wasn't always the same length. Sometimes he would cut a piece longer, but I wasn't allowed to make excuses."

Nysa took notes on the pad in her lap. "So, you couldn't defend yourself by explaining that it was his shortcoming that he was spanking you for, not yours."

"Right. Well, some of it was his, and some was mine. I would be daydreaming, thinking about a book I was reading or something, and sometimes I wouldn't realize that I had a few pieces out of line until there was a whole stack on top of them. I would just take the beating rather than unstack all that wood to fix it. That part was on me."

"And you felt like you deserved punishment for that part?"

I squirmed, aware of where she was going. "He was trying to teach me to always do my best, and spanking was his motivation tool. I knew the system. I was going to get whipped every day no matter what I did, and it made sense to me that I was choosing a few extra licks rather than a half hour of extra work to fix my own mistakes. It was my fault for not paying more attention."

"So the sense of injustice wasn't about the work or the spankings. It was just about the swats you got for pieces of wood that he cut too long."

"Right." I tried to remember what it felt like, standing in front of the stack of wood after hours of work, waiting as my dad inspected it so I could take my licks. "Mostly."

"Okay. Let's do some processing." She handed me a set of paddles, small plastic discs with a wire coming out of them, one to hold in each hand. "Have I explained the bilateral stimulation part of EMDR therapy to you?"

I shook my head. "Not really. You told me we were going to use it, but not how it works."

"Okay. The ten-second version is that you hold on to these paddles while you're going through these scenarios in your head. They vibrate back and forth from hand to hand, and that helps your brain rewire the emotions that are attached to the memories. We're getting rid of the old negative junk and replacing it with a positive self-view."

"Okay, sounds good," I said. "Let's try it out."

The vibration buzzed back and forth when she turned it on, oscillating from hand to hand in a comforting way. I closed my eyes and leaned back in the chair as she directed my focus.

"I want you to go back to that time. How old were you?"

I shrugged, keeping my eyes closed. "Probably seven or eight in the beginning. I did the firewood for years, though, until we finally got an electric furnace."

"We'll go back to the earliest point, so seven-year-old Justin. I want you to stand beside seven-year-old Justin while he's waiting for his dad to get the paddle. Put yourself completely in that moment. What is he feeling? What is he thinking?"

We sat in silence for a minute. I pictured the pile of wood, straight and square, but not perfect. Not quite good enough to avoid being punished. I'd probably get four or five swats, so that wasn't too bad.

She shut off the paddles a minute later. "Did you get there?"

I nodded.

"Okay, good. Let's rate your starting point. On a scale of one to ten, with ten being maximum disturbance, how disturbing is this moment paired with the thought, *I am a victim of injustice*?"

"About a three."

Nysa dropped her pen on the clipboard and stared at me in mock exasperation. "A three? Really?"

I smiled sheepishly. "Well, it's not like it owns me today, but it's still a little disturbing when I think about it."

"How much did it disturb you then? Where would seven-year-old Justin rate it? I want you to immerse yourself in that moment and feel the feelings."

I took a deep breath and let it out with a sigh. She was right—I was holding back. If I was going to get anything out of the therapy, I needed to do it all the way. I chalked my first answer up to a rookie mistake, forgave myself for being new at it, and tried again.

The scene was easy to picture. It was the fall of 1983, chilly, but not yet freezing. We were in the backyard of the house in Dewey, Oklahoma. The stack of wood between the poles was in front of me, parallel with the back porch. To the right, the pile of wood waiting to be split and stacked lay where it had been thrown or rolled out of the back of the truck. I couldn't lift most of the logs, so my dad didn't make me stack the wood until after I split it.

To the left, past the door and the end of the closed-in porch, were the driveway and the free-standing garage, faded white paint peeling off the ancient lumber. My dad's dark blue '67 Barracuda sat under the A-frame, a tarp covering the open engine compartment. It was always broken down, and helping my dad work on it was another job that consumed a lot of my childhood.

I pictured myself standing there, four feet tall instead of my now six feet, two inches, my blond hair combed forward instead of back, the square brown plastic-framed glasses sliding down my nose. My dad stood at one end of the pile near the porch steps, a red checkered bandana covering his long dark braids and his bushy black beard hanging down to the bib of his dirty blue overalls. That wasn't quite right, though, was it? He didn't start growing his hair and beard out for a few more years yet, not until I was about ten. It was hard to remember him before the beard and the braids.

I could smell him, though: a mixture of solvent and metal and sweat, the odor of his job as a machinist that never left him, a smell that still made my guts twist up in a knot to this day. He looked like a biker, hairy and swarthy and irritated. Any minute now, he would tell me to start counting the pieces of wood sticking out of the pile. If I tried to skip one, I'd get two swats for it instead.

It was easy to picture everything, even though I hadn't thought about it in many years. Capturing the feelings was harder. It was like watching a movie with the sound turned down, and Nysa clearly wasn't going to let me get away with leaving it like that.

I tried to meld with my younger self, to be a child again and feel my emotions. As I became one with my child mind, I was flooded with impotence and rage. It wasn't a pure feeling, or omnidirectional. Part of my rage was directed at myself for not doing a better job. I knew there were at least five pieces of wood out of place. I'd already counted them, shoving in the ones that could move deeper into the pile. Part of my rage was directed at the paddle sticking out of the leg-pocket of my dad's overalls. The fact that he brought it out with him indicated that he didn't consider it likely that I'd managed to make a perfect stack. It was a reasonable assumption— I'd never made a perfect stack. I just couldn't seem to do it.

On some level, I was angry at the pointlessness of it all. Tomorrow morning, I would carry a quarter of the stack inside the back porch and refill the wood box by the stove, starting the whole sequence over again. It was an endless loop— splitting wood, stacking it, telling dad how many swats I should get for it, taking it inside and burning it to heat the house, over and over, relentless. I imagined that we were ants in an ant farm and that someone was watching us. How pathetic and ridiculous would we look to them?

I clenched my fists, the burning shame at my inability to get it right just once threatening to overspill my eyes. I forced the tears back, knowing they would just create more anger from my dad. *I haven't even given you anything to cry about yet,* he would say. *Do you want me to?* He pulled the board out of his pocket, indicating with the tip for me to turn around and bend over. I hated myself as much as him as I shuffled over and grabbed my knees.

Nysa's voice pulled me back to the present. "On a scale of one to ten, how disturbing is it to say, *I am a victim*?"

"Ten," I whispered. The paddles buzzed in my hands, left, right, left, right.

"On a scale of one to seven, with one being completely false and seven being completely true, how would you rate this statement? *I am good enough.*"

"One."

"I want you to focus on that feeling and think about the statement. *I am good enough.* Feel it. Focus on the statement. Thirty seconds."

I nodded mutely and shut my eyes, squeezing the paddles in my fists. Now that I'd turned on the feelings that had been kept suppressed for so long, they were threatening to crush me. They were so powerful, so vast. How had I ever kept them at bay? Maybe I hadn't. Maybe I just held on to the rage and ignored the rest and convinced myself that I was fine.

I wanted to tell my seven-year-old self that things were going to turn out okay, that life was going to be great for him eventually. But honestly, what could I say, knowing that he had another twenty-five years to go before that started to happen? That was four lifetimes for me at that age, something I couldn't even fathom then. It would be cruel to tell a child he wasn't even a quarter of the way through the bad part. I gripped the paddles tightly, trying to draw some sort of calming energy from them.

"Relax your shoulders," Nysa said. "Take a few deep breaths and let go of the tension."

I pulled in air through my nose, expanding my chest until my lungs could hold no more, then let it out slowly as I tried to put the two contradictory thoughts together over the top of the image. Rage. Helplessness. *I am good enough.* Rage. Helplessness. *I am good enough.*

I stared at the pile. Every day in the winter I would walk home from school and stack wood. It had to be done before my dad got home from work. There were never any excuses allowed.

My dad stood beside me, his smell permeating every breath I took. I wondered if my resentment was as palpable to him as his anger was to me. I hated him, feared him, loved him, wanted to please him, and lived for his approval. How did he feel about me? That if he whipped me enough, I would eventually become perfect? That if he pointed out all my failures, I would work harder to avoid them? That if he never acknowledged my successes, that I would commit myself to a path of continuous self-improvement? That if he was demanding enough, I might actually become the kind of son he could be proud of?

I wanted to rip the board out of his hand and attack him with it. I wanted to scream at him, to shout in his face that I worked hard every day to stack the wood, along with all my other chores, and all he ever did was whip me for it. How could he not see the pointlessness of my existence? No matter what I did, he was going to whip me. What was my reward? Fewer swats?

The paddles fell silent in my hands, bringing me back to the present.

"What's coming up?" Nysa asked.

I shook my head. "A lot of negativity. I wanted to explain to my dad how his system was flawed, but that wasn't allowed. He would never admit that I was right, even if it was obvious."

"What was the flaw in the system?"

"That… that I was going to get whipped no matter how hard I worked." The more I thought about the situation, the more it became clear to me that I was looking at things wrong. "Maybe the injustice wasn't that some of the wood was cut too long. I think it was actually that I was going to get punished no matter what. The impossible carrot he dangled was that if I did a good enough job, I wouldn't get spanked, but I never seemed to achieve it. I just kept trying, kept doing all the things, and kept getting punished."

"How did that make you feel about yourself? What truths did you form about you as a result of that?"

I thought for a moment. "I felt that no matter what, I would always fall short of the mark. I could do things, but I wasn't capable of doing anything right. I felt like a loser."

Nysa nodded. "Did you ever give up or rebel against his orders?"

"No, I always did the work, trying to show him that I could be better. I wasn't able to just outright defy him and not do something he told me to do."

"Why not?"

I shrugged. "He had me completely cowed. A whipping for not meeting the expectation was one thing. A whipping for not doing it at all? I couldn't even imagine that. It would be suicide, like throwing trash all over the yard."

"Okay, one to ten, where is your disturbance?"

"Ten."

"One to seven, *I am good enough.*"

"One."

"Let's do it again. Put yourself fully in the moment, and just go with your thoughts."

The paddles began buzzing in my hands, and I let out a deep breath.

Rage. Helplessness. *I am good enough.* Rage. Helplessness. *I am good enough.* The anger was subsiding. It was like a brush fire. At first, the flames were tall as they consumed all the leaves and twigs, but then they died back. The logs burned long and slow, but the flames sank into the coals.

What were the facts of the situation? If I took all the emotion out of it, what actually happened? The house was heated by a woodstove. My job was to split the wood, stack it behind the house in the rack, and fill the wood box beside the stove. I did that. I did it every day. As a result of my actions, the house was warm in the winter. Yes, I got a spanking for it instead of gratitude, but that wasn't because I failed to do my job. That was because my dad didn't know how to be a father. He was displaying his own shortcomings, not punishing me for mine.

I did the work. I fulfilled my part of the obligation. I succeeded. I was good enough to get the job done. What did it matter if a few pieces stuck out of the pile? It didn't matter at all. It was a pointless detail. Again, that was my dad, probably still unconsciously trying to get approval from his own father.

The paddles stopped buzzing. "What's coming up?"

My eyes opened, and I stared at the lamp in front of me. "I'm starting to realize that this whole charade was probably more about my dad than it was about me."

"Hold on to that," Nysa said. "One to ten, disturbance."

"Four."

"One to seven, *I'm good enough.*"

"Four."

"Let's do it again. Keep following that train of thought, that it's not about you. What was really going on there?" She turned the paddles back on, and I closed my eyes.

My dad's behavior was the result of his upbringing. When I was a child, his sisters told me how their dad had treated him when he was growing up. He was the oldest of the four kids, and while I had a hard time envisioning my kindly grandpa as a hardnosed taskmaster who was quick with the belt and slow with his praise, they assured me that my dad grew up the same way I was growing up. That knowledge did little to pacify me then, but the fact that someone cared enough to reach out to me was a comfort like I had never known. I was helpless, yes, but that wasn't the end of the world. My dad was doing what he knew how to do. The fact that he hadn't managed to break the cycle was sad, but I was different than he was. I would break the cycle. *I am good enough.*

Nysa shut the paddles off. "What's coming up?"

"I realized that the big-picture goal was to keep the flow of firewood going so we could stay warm, and I totally accomplished that. I got whipped for doing it, but not because I didn't get it done. That was just my dad being confused about parenting and taking his frustrations out on me. It was never about me or the firewood."

Nysa smiled broadly. "That's great! You were never a failure. You were just measuring yourself by the wrong things. You had a difficult task, and you worked hard and got it done, over and over, even though you got punished for doing it instead of praised. And you never gave up, you never broke. That's huge! Can you see what an accomplishment that is?"

I nodded, feeling a bit dizzy from the new perspective. "When I look at it like that, I feel like I was amazing. I worked hard, and it mattered. And it's so obvious to me how my thoughts on work, and authority, and punishment and all that got so skewed. My dad taught me that no matter how hard I tried, it wasn't good enough, that I'd fall short and get punished. I never really saw what I was accomplishing because I was too busy resenting him. And then I carried that same attitude into the working world and resented every boss I ever had. What a mess."

"Right?" Nysa laughed. "But you recognized that, and you've changed your attitude because of it. That's the most important thing. You gained new insights and created new behaviors. The only failure would be if you saw the error of your ways but kept acting the same. Does that make sense?"

"Definitely. I made mistakes based on bad information, but as soon as I got new information, I changed. That's a win."

"Exactly." She took the paddles from me and began winding up the cord. "Now then, how can you apply that to AT&T?"

It took me a moment to map out the connection. "I would say that AT&T isn't targeting me. They aren't out to get me, they're just inept. My suffering at their hands is basically the same as my suffering at my dad's hands in that I just happened to be the one standing there. I have to stop taking it personally. It's not about me, and it's not an indicator of my value."

"Let's check in. One to ten, disturbance."

"Two."

"One to seven, *I am good enough*."

"Six."

"Nicely done." Nysa rewarded me with a grin. "The hard part is remembering that in the heat of the moment, but between the EMDR, writing this down for your book, and good old-fashioned practice, you'll get it. Now, let's put all that stuff in your Pensieve. The feelings, the images, seven-year-old Justin, everything."

My Pensieve was an artifact stolen from Professor Dumbledor in the *Harry Potter* series, a magic bowl where I could store things outside my brain; thoughts, memories, feelings, whatever. Nysa had simply told me to imagine a container where I would put these things, but I read way too much fantasy to be content with a box or a tub. Mine was an engraved silver bowl, mysterious, with a layer of fog on the surface hiding the contents. On the inside, it was The Oasis, from *Ready Player One.* A digital universe with thousands of planets and worlds from every book or movie I wanted. That gave me unlimited storage space, and it also gave me a safe and interesting place to put my child-self. He could explore Treasure Island, or fly in a rocket with Tom Swift Jr., or ride bikes with the Bobbsey Twins as they solved mysteries and had epic good times.

I closed my eyes and visualized myself collecting all of the feelings connected to the firewood stack. Part of me wanted to hang on to the anger, and I really had to work on transferring it all to the Pensieve. Next, I rescued my seven-year-old self. One of my favorite books at that age was *The Hobbit*, so I wrapped my arms around him and teleported to the Shire in front of Bilbo Baggins' house. I watched for a moment as he looked around in amazement, then came back to the chair in my therapist's office and opened my eyes.

"How do you feel?"

"Empty. Weird. Drained. Exhausted."

"Agitated?"

"No, very calm."

"Good. If you need to talk to seven-year-old Justin or process any of this stuff, you know where he is, right?"

"Yep."

"Okay, get out of here. I'll see you next Thursday."

I drove home in a daze, trying to put things in perspective. The idea that I had succeeded at the thousands of tasks I'd been assigned as a kid upended the very foundation of my whole understanding of my childhood. That was a lot to wrap my head around. My core identity was built on the knowledge that I always fell short of the mark. Changing that one tenet had massive implications, and it was going to take some time for the dust to settle. If every therapy session was as earth-shattering as this one, it was going to be an interesting year.

Chapter 3

I SAT IN THE NOW-FAMILIAR CHAIR in Nysa's office. We were talking about my mother-in-law, and why I was so quick to lose my temper with her. I stared at the front tire on the motorcycle picture. My eyes always seemed to rest there. The motorcycle was covered in words, and the forks holding the wheel boasted a sticker that I found apropos: *Journey*.

"You explain something to her, like why you're trying to reduce your plastic consumption, and she smiles and nods and then goes out and buys ten packets of shredded cheese instead of one big block," Nysa said, flicking a piece of lint off her sleeve.

"Exactly," I said. "I can't decide if she just doesn't care, or if she's actively trying to spite me. It's not just with the plastic, it's everything."

"That makes you mad, of course. What's the feeling underneath the anger?"

That was harder to put my finger on. I had spent hours explaining all the reasons why she shouldn't take the dogs to the grocery store. Hours. We sat down together and watched a video by a veterinarian she knew and respected. He was in a car in a grocery store parking lot with the windows down a few inches and held a big thermometer and a stopwatch so we could see how hot it got in the car and how quickly. And yet, the very next day, she came home from the grocery store, opened the car door, and out hopped the dogs.

How did that make me feel? Exasperated, ignored, patronized, and marginalized. A pattern was beginning to emerge. "I think I'm offended because she pretends to agree with me, but then her actions prove that she was just pacifying me in the moment. It's like what I say doesn't matter to her. I don't matter."

"*I don't matter.*" Nysa wrote it down on her pad. "Does that statement resonate with you? Have you felt it before?"

"Oh, I'm old friends with that one. We go way back. Not so much these days, but it used to be one of my big insecurities." Apparently, I wasn't as far past it as I'd thought. That rankled a bit.

"Let's talk about that. What's your earliest memory of feeling like you don't matter?"

I'd spent so much of my life trying to pretend like the first half of it never happened that it was hard to dredge up specific memories at first. On the other side of that coin, it was funny how I remembered particular elements and details once I got going.

"Before my sister was born, life wasn't too bad most of the time. Everything changed when she came into the picture."

"In what way?"

"Well, my dad isn't my biological father. I was a package deal with my mom, so I think finally having his own kid was part of it. I'm sure the additional expense of another child was a stress factor, too. We moved right before she was born, and my dad got a new job around that same time."

"How old were you?"

"I was six when my sister was born. Exactly six. She was born on my birthday. It happened to fall on Thanksgiving that year."

"And I'm guessing all the focus was on her, and you got shuffled to the back."

"Yeah, I'm sure that was an underlying cause. I don't remember acting out more than usual, but that would be an obvious reason for me to be bad. I can't remember if it was the Christmas right after she was born, or the following Christmas. It was one of those, '81 or '82. Anyway, I got up on Christmas morning and raced into the living room, and there was a neat bundle of sticks from the tree out in the front yard with a red ribbon tied around it in a bow and a yellow Post-it Note with my name on it."

"Were there any other presents under the tree?"

"Oh yeah, my little sister had a pile of presents. Not huge, you know, but five or six things. We were poor, so there was never a ton of stuff, but the only thing there for me was the sticks. I thought they were teaching me a lesson, and that after I cried and promised to be a good boy, I'd get my real presents."

Nysa raised her eyebrows.

I shook my head. "It didn't happen. Santa doesn't bring presents to bad kids."

Nysa lifted her hand and started to say something, but then trailed off. She shook her head as if she didn't believe me. "Your parents gave you a bundle of sticks for Christmas? Because you were bad?"

I nodded.

"Justin, that's beyond messed up. It's not okay. You recognize that, right?"

I shrugged. "It *is* messed up. But I think there were probably some other factors that I didn't think about then. They didn't have any money, and they talked about that all the time. I knew they couldn't afford anything beyond making the bills and buying food, and sometimes not even that. We lived on pinto beans for months at a time, or white rice."

"Justin, listen to yourself. You're making excuses for them. Poor people don't try to make their kids feel like it's their own fault they didn't get any presents. They tell them how sorry they are for not being able to afford more, but that they love them, and someday when things get better, they'll have a big Christmas to make up for the hard times. Do you see the difference?"

"Yes, I get it." I realized I was being defensive, and forced a small grin. "I guess I'm afraid that I'm painting a bad picture of them, and I don't want you to think it was always like that. They weren't horrible people. They just did some messed up things sometimes."

Nysa looked skeptical as she tossed me the paddles. "Let's get into this. Six-year-old Justin, Christmas morning, a bundle of sticks while your baby sister, who doesn't even know what a present is, gets a pile of them. The negative cognition is, *I don't matter*, right?"

I nodded.

"What's the feeling that we want to transition to?"

I thought for a moment. "That I have value? I do matter?"

She wrote it down. "*I have value*. Let's work with that. I want you to go back there, back to Christmas of 1981. Get in that moment, and pair it with the phrase, *I don't matter*."

I settled back in the chair and closed my eyes. The paddles vibrated in my hands, left, right, left, right. I tried to picture my childhood bedroom. I remembered the yellow, steel-framed bunk beds. Back then my stuffed animals lived on the top bunk, and I lived on the bottom. Later, once my sister was out of the crib, she slept on the bottom bunk, and I moved to the top. This event was before that, so I tried to remember living on the bottom. Sometimes I would take my blanket and tuck it under the mattress on the top bunk and let it drape down to the floor, creating a fort. It was a good fort because I could squeeze down to the floor on the backside between the bed and the wall and be under the bed, and no one would know where I was. If I was feeling especially acrobatic, I could use the windowsill to worm my way up to the top bunk from the back side, staying hidden behind the teddy bears and Cookie Monster.

Cookie Monster. That opened a fresh set of memories. My parents were staunchly anti-television. As a result of that, I had a Cookie Monster stuffed animal, which a relative had given me for Christmas at some point, but I had never seen Sesame Street, and I didn't know who Cookie Monster was. I still loved him.

Back on task. I moved to the open door of the bedroom, which led to the kitchen. On the outside of my door to the right was about six inches of wall space, ending in a corner. Six inches to the left of that was the doorway between the kitchen and the dining room. I spent a lot of time standing in that corner, my mom's go-to punishment. I learned that if I got just the right angle with the light, I could see the reflection of my eye in my glasses. I couldn't quite look myself right in the eye, but I could get really close. Making the effort passed a lot of time when I was supposed to be thinking about what I'd done to end up in the corner in the first place.

On through the dining room, over the big furnace grate in the vinyl tile floor, and into the living room. Straight ahead, to the left of the front door, was the Christmas tree. It was also in front of a window, centered on the front wall. It had the big '70's lights on it— red, blue, green, yellow, probably a serious fire hazard. We didn't have tinsel, but I remember that we had made a big bowl of popcorn and strung it on a thread with a needle. There was a mason jar lid with a Polaroid picture of me on it that I'd made in preschool hanging from a red ribbon, along with some old ornaments from my mother's childhood. And underneath, also secured in a red ribbon, was the bundle of sticks.

The sticks were about two feet long, and the bundle was probably eight or ten inches in diameter. My dad must have gone out the night before and collected them from the yard. The red ribbon made a single loop around the center of the bundle and was tied in a neat bow. That was probably my mom's doing. I tried to remember the handwriting on the Post-it Note. I couldn't picture it, but that was almost certainly my mom, too. My dad wasn't very strong with reading and writing.

The paddles stopped vibrating, lifting me out of the memory.

"What's coming up?"

I was embarrassed about getting sidetracked, but it was important to be honest with her. "I was looking around the house, trying to remember things. I didn't actually think about my statement yet. But I did get to the tree and the bundle of sticks."

She nodded. "What kind of feelings came up as you looked around?"

"Nothing terrible," I said. "I was mostly surprised about all the things I haven't thought about in thirty-five years."

"Okay, let's go again. Focus on the sticks and how you feel knowing that's what you got for Christmas. Pair that with *I don't matter.*"

The paddles began their rhythmic buzzing again, back and forth. I closed my eyes and went back to the living room. Instead of treating it like a museum, I tried to imagine that I was really there, as if I had traveled through time.

My parents were in their bedroom, which was on the other side of the front door. The bedroom door was open, my dad's dark blue felt bathrobe with the neon green trim and belt (made by my mom) hanging from the top as always, and I was sure that a creaking floorboard beneath the thick carpet would give me away. I wasn't forty-four-year-old Justin, tall and strong and confident and successful. I was six, and I lived my life from one negative experience to the next, and I was afraid. I tore my eyes away from the darkened bedroom doorway and looked under the Christmas tree.

There were five or six wrapped presents, all for my sister. They each had the same wrapping paper, a beige background with red stockings printed all over it. I recognized it as the same thing my presents had been wrapped in the year before. A sprinkling of fir needles dusted the presents and the green felt under the tree. The purpose of the felt was to catch the tree debris and keep it out of the carpet, and I wasn't supposed to play near it lest I mess it up.

I don't matter. To the left lay my bundle of sticks. They hadn't just *not* gotten me Christmas presents— they'd gone to the trouble of collecting sticks and wrapping them in a bow. They put effort and thought into it. They were trying to tell me something.

What did that make me feel? Anger? Rejection? Shame? I felt shame, for sure, and not just a little bit. Wave after wave of shame rolled over me. I was so bad they didn't want me around. They were trying to tell me that I didn't belong there anymore, that I wasn't part of the family. I was so embarrassed that I didn't even know how to respond. I was angry at them for rejecting me, but I was even more angry at myself for driving them to it. Angry and ashamed. *I have value.* I didn't feel like I had any value. I felt like shit.

The paddles became still, pulling me back to the present. "On a scale of one to ten, how distressing is the bundle of sticks combined with the idea, *I don't matter*?" Nysa asked.

My throat was too dry to speak on the first try, and I had to swallow twice before I could answer. "Ten." I kept my eyes closed.

"On a scale of one to seven, how true does this statement feel? *I have value.*"

"One," I whispered.

"Okay, let's do it again. Bundle of sticks. *I don't matter*, and *I have value.*"

The paddles came back on, a reassuring presence as they buzzed, left, right, left, right. This time my parents were in the living room, sitting on the floor. My baby sister was tucked inside an enormous stocking, and they were taking a picture of her on my mom's Kodak 110 camera. I was sitting against the wall beside the tree near my bundle of sticks, wishing I could slip out the window and run away, never to return.

Why didn't I leave? Why didn't I at least go to my room, where I could disappear into a book? Because I wasn't allowed to leave. I was being ignored, but it was part of my punishment. I couldn't escape. I had to sit there and see what my bad behavior had caused me to miss out on.

I pictured a treasure chest on an empty beach and tried to jam all my feelings inside of it. I didn't want to show them how bad they'd hurt me, how the sticks had cut me right down to the bone. I wanted to pretend like I didn't care. My body betrayed me, though, and I sat there with clenched fists and red eyes, my knees drawn up protectively to my chest. *I hate you, I hate you, I hate you!* I was screaming inside my head, screaming things I would never be bold enough to say out loud. My dad would whip me for mouthing off like that, and God would probably send me to burn in Hell for not honoring my father and mother. I was helpless, and I hated that feeling. My only solace was to embrace the rage because it made me feel powerful, at least a little bit.

I don't matter. I fantasized about how they would feel if I died. If I got one of Dad's pistols out of his closet and blew my brains out, then they would feel guilty. I knew where he kept the .357 Magnum revolver. Mom would think about me every night when she had to wash the dishes and take the trash out, as I wouldn't be there to do it. Dad would have to get his own wrenches when he worked on the car, and hold his own flashlight. Maybe then he'd realize that I'd been making a bigger contribution than he ever gave me credit for. And how would I feel? I would feel nothing. And feeling nothing would be an improvement.

I have value. I did have value. I did a lot of chores. No one ever thanked me for it or told me I'd done a good job, but I worked my ass off. It wasn't that I didn't have value, it was that no one ever recognized my value or communicated that to me. All they ever did was give me my list of chores, doublecheck that I did everything right, and punish me for any shortcomings they found.

The paddles stopped. "What's coming up?" Nysa asked.

I tried to put my thoughts into a coherent sentence. "I was thinking about all the things I did back then, my contributions. I had a lot of chores, even at that age."

"And?"

I stretched my legs out in front of me. "It seems to me that I wanted them to recognize the effort I made instead of taking it for granted."

"Did you ever say that to them?"

I started to say that I hadn't, but a new memory popped up. "I did. I just remembered that. I remember listing out all the things I did. I think I was defending myself for getting caught reading a book when I was supposed to be doing something else."

"And what did your dad say? Was it your dad?"

"Yeah. He told me that he went to work every day and earned the money that paid for everything, and I never thanked him for doing that. I couldn't argue. It was true."

Nysa shook her head as she wrote a note on her pad. "One to ten, how disturbing is the bundle of sticks combined with *I don't matter*?"

"Seven."

"Okay, good. One to seven, how true does it feel to say, *I have value*?"

"Three or four."

"Let's do it again."

I sat in front of the window beside the Christmas tree. The cold December air seeped through the panes of glass, chilling the back of my neck. I realized with horror that when Christmas break was over, I would go back to school. What if someone asked me what kind of presents I got? What if Ms. Cavin asked me? Not only was she my teacher, but she also went to our church. I couldn't possibly tell her the truth, but it would be wrong to lie. What a terrible dilemma this was. I was far too embarrassed to tell anyone that I was so bad that I got sticks for Christmas. What would they think of me? No one would want to be friends with a kid that bad.

Adult me was almost amused that it never occurred to my six-year-old self that people might think badly of my parents, rather than me. Would that have changed anything? I thought not. I was still convinced at that age that it was a sin to go against your parents, especially to try to publicize their behavior. I was in enough inner turmoil trying to deal with the sin of my smart mouth, and that was small potatoes on the sin list compared to dishonoring my parents.

I have value. I glanced at the sticks, then back to my mom and dad. They were opening presents for my sister. She lay on the floor and clutched at the wrapping paper, oblivious to the rattles and onesies pajamas she had received. It was all a charade. My value wasn't dependent on them. What had I been thinking? They were so wrapped up in their own world that they didn't even know me. I was in the background. No, that wasn't right. I might have been in *their* background, but I was front and center in my own life. *I have value.* I *did* have value. Fuck them and their sticks.

"One to ten, how disturbing are the sticks?"

"Three."

"What changed?"

"I was trying to ascertain my value from what I thought *they* thought my value was rather than how I felt about myself."

"Do you think the work you did was what gave you value?"

"Sure. I worked my ass off."

"Does the fact that you were a person with thoughts and feelings give you any value?"

It was a tougher question than it should have been. What did I value about myself? What did I value about other people? Was it work ethic? Character? The fact that we're alive? I valued most animals as much as people, and that's not based on work ethic or character. What *was* it based on?

"I see what you're saying," I said at last. "I was valuing myself based on my contribution to the household. It's the same system that I thought my dad used. I guess I don't really have an answer for what gives a person value, but it seems like it ought to be more than the number of chores they do, huh?"

"I would think so. Go back in and think about where your value comes from." She turned the paddles back on.

This time, I stood off to the side and looked at my child-self sitting by the window. How young I had been then, so full of energy and determination. The hostility radiated from my child face. What gave that little boy value? There had to be more than just the base allotment one gets for being alive.

While the fact that I did a lot of work couldn't be the base of my value, it still felt right to count it as something. I did things that kept the household functioning, and that's not nothing. I also had a blooming intellect. I devoured books and spent a lot of time thinking about what I'd read while doing other chores. Even then I was learning about people and the world, ethics and morals, and what kind of person I wanted to be. My attempts to learn and comprehend such things certainly gave me value.

I looked over at my dad. He was grinning at my sister and

shaking her tiny fist as she grasped his finger. Did she have more value than me? Less? Where did her value come from? She had none of the things that I considered my own sources of value, beyond simply being alive. Maybe that's all there really was. Maybe I was overthinking it.

The paddles fell still in my hands, and I opened my eyes.

"What did you come up with?" Nysa asked.

I let out a sigh. "More questions than answers. I mean, I came up with some things that I *think* gave me value, like trying to learn and develop my critical thinking skills, and the chores I did. But then I thought about my little sister. She was an infant. What gives her value? Just being alive? Is that all there is? I don't know."

"Maybe all those things are right," Nysa said. "Maybe it's living to your capacity that gives you value."

That gave me pause. *Living to my capacity*. The opposite would be merely existing at a minimum, making no effort to grow. The concept appealed to me. "Wow. That's like, that's heavy. I was all around it, but that hits the nail on the head. I like it a lot."

Nysa laughed. "Thank you! You made some good progress today. Let's stop there. When you write about this session for your book, try to dig deeper and find the full answers. Writing it out helps you continue processing, but it also lets you spend as much time as you need to get the full picture. You don't lose value as a human being by making mistakes or being imperfect. Recognizing opportunities to improve is important, but that's not the same thing as punishing yourself for having a flaw in what you did. Keep thinking about what it is that gives you value, and make sure you take note of the things that trigger negative feelings and see if they really take away from your value or not. We're consciously reconfiguring your whole value system, so be thorough with your examination of those insecurities. We already know that most of them are based on false ideas, and we want to root those out."

"I will," I promised. It seemed a staggering task, but I'd already tasted the success of my efforts, and I wanted more.

"And talk to Erica about it," she said. "She probably has a very different perspective on self-value than you do. As your wife, she wants to support you, right? Tell her what your weak areas are so she can help you make them stronger."

I nodded slowly. "Yeah, that's a good idea. She's been asking for ways to help me. That's perfect!"

She winked and made a shooing gesture. "You're welcome. Now go on, get out of here. See you soon."

I sat in the parking lot for a while, trying to get my brain back in the present. 1981 was a long time ago, and Oklahoma was a long way away, but it was all right there in the front of my mind. The porch swing, the girl next door who would move in a few years and be replaced by a boy who would beat me up in the street at the urging of his mother, the long bike rides out in the country, the fantasies of suicide, the longing to escape. Thirty-eight years and a thousand miles was really just a thought away. *I have value.* I didn't understand that until I was in my mid-thirties. It seemed like an important thing for a kid to know.

Chapter 4

"Tell me about the trash can," Nysa said. Today she was in a tight plaid button-down shirt and jeans, her dark purple hair pulled back in a ponytail. "It's the next thing on your trauma timeline. What's that about?"

Unlike most of my other childhood experiences, which rarely crossed my mind, I thought about the trash can several times a year. It didn't usually evoke a major emotional response, but it always popped up when I was feeling down on myself, a way to confirm my negative beliefs.

"It was one of the big roller carts that you put down by the curb for the trashman," I said. "Tall, green, plastic. This one had a removable lid, rather than a lid on a hinge. We had two of them. They weren't as much of a cube as the one we have at home now. These were tall and skinny, and rectangular."

I sat sideways to Nysa, staring at the motorcycle picture. Sometimes I wished she had a couch and a big dark office like shrinks in the movies, rather than that small, drab room. She wouldn't look right behind a big expensive desk, though. It wasn't her style. This wasn't either, but I didn't know what an appropriate office for her would look like.

"My dad was the primary disciplinarian. Sometimes my mom would spank me, but usually she would wait until my dad got home and have him do it. She had other punishments, though. I stood in the corner a lot, and I couldn't tell you how many times I've washed my mouth out with soap. Homemade lye soap is the worst, in case you were wondering. It burns your tongue. The rest of them just taste bad." I grimaced at the memory.

"Anyway, sometimes if I got in trouble, she would make me empty the trash bags out of one of the dumpsters and drag it up inside the back porch. One of her sewing machines was out there, so if she was working on a project out back, I had to climb inside the trash can and sit and wait for my dad to get home to spank me instead of standing in the corner in the sewing room."

"She made you sit inside the trash can?"

I nodded. "Yeah. I think it was so that I wasn't reading a book or playing while I waited on my punishment. If I was in the trash can, I was thinking about what I did."

Nysa wrote for nearly a minute, her pen flying across the page. "How long would she keep you in there?"

"I really don't know. Maybe an hour or two? Long enough for my legs to go to sleep, sometimes."

"Did she put the lid on it?"

"Yeah, but sideways, so it didn't seal off the air. The can was wider than it was deep, a rectangle. There was a good gap for air and some light."

"That was thoughtful of her." She didn't try to disguise the scorn in her voice. "How did it make you feel about yourself?"

Even though I knew this question was coming, I didn't have an answer. I tried to remember sitting in the trash can and what I thought about. "It was a combination of things. There was a lot of trepidation about my dad coming home and the whipping that would happen, but I was also repulsed by the grossness of the whole thing. I remember trying not to let my skin touch anything."

Nysa waited in silence as I closed my eyes and tried to go back to that moment. The first thing I remembered was the smell. Rotting garbage smells the same worldwide. Pungent, cloying, the scent of death and decay that always makes me gag. The smell brought forth images— the dim light making its way into the can, just enough for me to see the trash stuck to the stained surface in front of my face, but not enough to identify it. The sensation of wetness as the seat of my pants became soaked through with the slime I was sitting in. Cupping my hands around my nose and mouth, sealing my tee shirt against my face as an air filter. Wishing that I had a modicum of self-control so I could avoid getting myself in these situations.

"I know it sounds ridiculous, but I was more upset with myself than anything."

Nysa's face tightened. "Justin, she made you sit in a trash can. That's not okay. How would you react if someone made you do that today, or if you saw someone else put their kid in a dumpster?"

"No, I get that. The system was flawed, and I recognized that on some level, even then, but I also knew the rules and the consequences. I blamed myself for not realizing when I was doing something that was going to land me there. That was the part I felt like I should be able to control, but somehow I couldn't."

Nysa looked up, rocking her head from side to side as if debating the merits of my argument. "All right, I'll buy that, for now. What was the behavior that got you in trouble that you couldn't control?"

It was always my mouth. It operated ten seconds ahead of my brain, and there was no filter in place. My wit was sharp and quick, much faster than the part of my brain that tried to protect me from danger. I also had a complex and well-developed sense of humor. My dad often told me not to be a smartass, and I would promptly respond that if I'd ever had any brains in my butt, he'd beaten them into oblivion long ago.

I was also a musical child. If someone started a sentence with a particular word or phrase that was familiar, my mind would instantly jump to the song and lyrics that followed. *So?* A hanging question that my mother employed when she wanted an explanation, always brought to mind the do-re-mi song, and I would blurt out, *a needle pulling thread.* It was funny to me, a six-year-old boy, and sometimes my mother would reward me with a grin. I probably kept saying it because of that, hoping for a moment of approval. It must have been worth the risk of washing my mouth out with soap for being a smart mouth, which happened as often as the smile, at least in my memory.

"I'm having a hard time remembering a specific instance," I said. "But it was always a sarcastic statement of some sort. I'd be playing, and my mom would tell me to slow down, or quiet down, and I'd pop off with some smart comment. If I was playing airplane, I'd tell her that I couldn't slow down, because I had to maintain airspeed or the plane would crash and everyone would die, and that would be her fault. Or if she was on the phone when I came racing into the room, she'd shush me, and I'd freeze in place, like a movie on pause. The second she hung up the phone, I'd reanimate, full volume, full speed. Or I'd be reading a book instead of washing dishes, or whatever chore I was supposed to be doing, and when she caught me, I'd say something like, *I'm going to get in trouble for something, so I might as well do something to deserve it.*"

"It sounds like you were being a normal kid, aside from that last part."

"Yeah, but I was argumentative about things. I needed to understand why. Why I had to stop this or not do that, and it needed to be logical. If it wasn't, I'd explain the error in their reasoning. That got me in a lot of trouble, especially with my dad."

"So, you were getting in trouble for arguing instead of just doing as you were told."

I nodded.

"Tell me about a specific instance where you tried to make a logical argument about something."

I scrolled through my memories, trying to find a suitable event. I settled on the endlessly broken-down car in the driveway, with my dad inside the engine compartment.

"Working on the car," I said slowly, trying to put myself there. "My dad was always working on the car, and I had to be out there helping him." A sudden realization hit me.

"I saw that," Nysa said with a smirk. "What just happened?"

"I've spent my whole life thinking my dad knew how to do everything. I thought he was a master mechanic, master carpenter, master plumber, master electrician, all of it. But when I take my truck to the repair shop, they fix whatever's wrong in an hour or two, a day at the most. My dad would spend weeks doing a repair, every night after work, all day on the weekends. It just occurred to me that he wasn't very good at it. It took him way too long to do things, and fixing one thing always led to another problem. He worked on the car for ten years, and it still wasn't running when he sold it so we could move. I can't believe I never realized that."

Nysa rolled her eyes theatrically. "Justin, you can't even admit that your dad was abusive. Is it really a stretch to think that you wouldn't question his supposed expertise in something? You never questioned anything he did. You hated it, you resented it, you rebelled against it, but you never questioned it."

I was stunned into silence. The shock of seeing the elephant that'd been standing in my blind spot all my life was more than a little overwhelming, even though it was the third or fourth elephant I'd discovered. What else didn't I know?

"Okay, working on the car," Nysa prompted. "What happened?"

I brought my focus back to the car with an effort, looking at my dad. He sat on the radiator in his faded blue overalls, hunched over the engine. He was humming a tuneless song, as he often did, though he never listened to the radio except when he was driving. I was standing on a block of wood so I could see where to shine the flashlight.

"My dad sent me for a wrench. A 9/16 box end is what he called it. *Go get me a 9/16 box end.* Standing in front of the toolbox, which was taller than I was with lots of drawers, all of them packed with tools, sometimes I felt stupid because I wasn't sure what I was looking for. Or, like this time, I was pretty sure I knew what I was looking for, but it wasn't there. I opened the wrench drawer and dug through the deep, cluttered mess, desperately trying to rush because the longer it took me, the madder he would be. I couldn't find it. I took all the wrenches out and put them back, one at a time. It wasn't there."

I took a deep breath and let it out slowly, forcing myself to relax in the chair. My eyes remained closed. I didn't want to lose the moment, but the stress of it was almost physically painful.

"You're okay," Nysa whispered.

"I had to make a decision," I said, straightening my unwilling fingers and planting my hands on my legs. "I could start looking in other places, which would take even longer, with no guarantee of success, or else go back and tell him I couldn't find it, which would also piss him off. It was a lose-lose situation."

"What did you do?"

"I went back and told him it wasn't in the drawer."

Letting out a deep breath, I put myself in the moment. 1985, Dewey, Oklahoma. I stood in the garage staring at the toolbox. The frustration with not being able to find the wrench combined with the knowledge that I was in trouble, but I couldn't freeze. I had to go tell him.

I ran back to the car, trying to save a few seconds from the time lost during my fruitless search. My dad was still sitting on the radiator, doing something that I couldn't see. As I ran, I practiced what I would say, trying to anticipate his response and prepare my defense.

"The wrench wasn't in the drawer," I said. In my head, I could hear my nine-year-old voice attempting to sound confident in my report so he wouldn't doubt my effort to find it. "I looked at every wrench."

He turned to look at me, scrunching his nose to push his glasses up, then tilting his head down so he could glare at me over the top of them. "Did you look anywhere else?"

"No, I was afraid it would take too long."

The workbench ran the length of one wall and was stacked with heaps of things. Parts to mowers, parts to cars, a disassembled vacuum cleaner, bowls of bolts for some long-forgotten project, tools, lumber, saws, drill presses, the vice, rags, and boxes of disassembled things. The table saw in the center of the floor was often the same way, as was the floor itself. There were trails that led through the piles of junk from one place to another. Add in the poor lighting and looking for a wrench that wasn't in the proper drawer wasn't simply hard, it was an exercise in futility. Not that I could say that, of course. Excuses were never acceptable, and criticizing the mess would mean volunteering to clean and organize it.

"If I go in there and find the 9/16 box end in the wrench drawer, I'm going to blister your ass. Are you still sure it ain't in there?"

I doubted myself, despite having removed every wrench from the drawer, but I nodded anyway. "I'm positive. Do I get to blister yours if it's not there?"

"You watch your smart mouth, boy, or you'll get a blistered ass anyway."

Nysa burst out laughing, and suddenly I was back in her office.

"Did you really say that to him?" she asked.

"Yeah. That's what I'm talking about. Of all the things for me to say, that's like asking him point blank to kick my ass." I shifted my voice to falsetto and added a British accent. "*Please sir, won't you whip me? Just a quick beating, please?*"

She clapped her hands, laughing freely. "That's awesome! Good for you for having the courage to point out the imbalance in the system, even if it was dangerous."

I shook my head. "It was pointless, though. It's not like he was going to see the light and change his evil ways, right? All it did was create more friction. And yet, I did it all the time, and I paid for it over and over and over. That's why I say that so much of it was my own doing. Yes, he was too hard on me, but I kept shoveling coal on the fire, day in and day out."

"You were trying to defend yourself, Justin. You were a child, and you didn't have any tools to cope with things, so you had to make them up as you went. You searched for equity and fairness. You used logic and humor because those were the things that made sense to you, and you found a way to get up every day and do it all over again. We've already established that you knew you were going to get a whipping every day no matter what, so what did you have to lose? Nothing. You kept making an effort instead of just withdrawing. Right?"

It was a drastically different perspective on things, and while I wasn't sure how this concept was connected to my mom putting me in the trash can, I still liked it. It made me more of a survivor and less of a victim. "That's a really good insight. I never looked at it that way."

She winked at me. "Was the wrench in the drawer?"

"No, it was under the car where he'd left it the night before."

"Did he apologize to you?"

I laughed bitterly. "No, he wasn't capable of that. But he didn't whip me, so that was basically an apology. I knew I was right, so I had that to hold on to. And obviously he knew I was right, even if he wouldn't admit it."

Nysa's eyes lit up, and she scribbled on her note pad. "Ooh, that was good. Let's say it again: *I knew I was right, so I had that to hold on to.* Let's tap that in with some bilateral stimulation, and then we'll go back to the trash can and do some processing." She handed me the paddles and looked over her notes. "Let's contrast *I feel stupid* with looking for the wrench. Remember your positive cognition, *I know I'm right.* You're at the toolbox. Start there, and just go with it."

I closed my eyes again and rested my hands on my lap, dropping my shoulders and loosening my jaw. Ten years of on-and-off-again meditation practice had taught me how to relax with a deep breath, and I used the technique to bring myself to a state of calm before slipping back into the past.

I stood in front of the toolbox. The filthy florescent fixture hanging over the mound of junk on the workbench did little to light up the inside of the drawer six feet away, and the waning daylight from outside barely made it past the open bay door at the front of the garage to my left. The jumble of wrenches lay in the open drawer in front of me, every size imaginable except the one I needed.

I feel stupid. I did, but it was more than that. I was frustrated. The only way this mission could go well was if I found the wrench right away, and that hadn't happened. I was insolent because no matter what, I would be in trouble for not returning with the wrench right away. There was no positive outcome available.

I know I'm right. The wrench wasn't in the drawer. I was trapped in a hopeless situation. The game was lost, but I still had to keep playing. When I gave up my turn, it would be my dad's turn, and I knew what his move would be. Being right didn't change my situation. It just made my frustration worse, and made me angrier knowing that I was going to be in trouble anyway.

The paddles stopped buzzing. "What's coming up?"

My eyes opened slowly. "All kinds of things. I was starting off in a bad spot, probably already peaked out on stress, because it's not like working on the car involved one trip to the toolbox. It happened repeatedly, and it went one of three ways every time. Either I found the wrench right away, I took too long but I found the wrench, or I took too long and didn't find the wrench. So, I would still be recovering from the previous trip."

"Did you get whipped every time?"

I shook my head. "No, he didn't get out of the engine compartment for that, unless he had to go find the tool himself. Usually, it was just verbal. That was equally stressful, though."

Nysa nodded. "For sure. Okay, so you started off in a bad mental state."

"Right. And when I couldn't find what he wanted, I would feel incompetent, stupid. I had teachers at school telling me I was a bright kid, putting me in the gifted program, but I couldn't find a wrench for the third time in an hour. It really messed with my sense of self. My dad berating me for it just compounded that doubt, and I would stand there in front of the toolbox wanting to disappear. The punishment loomed in the driveway like a hurricane, and I had to walk into it, over and over, feeling like a total loser.

"Was finding the wrench inside your control?" Nysa asked.

I shook my head. "Not if it wasn't where it's supposed to be."

"If it's in the wrench drawer, then finding it is on you. If it's not in the drawer, then it's outside your control, right?"

"Right."

"And if it's outside your control, and you still get in trouble for it?"

The pieces came together in my head with a nearly audible snap. "That's when my sense of injustice starts pegging out. I know I'm going to suffer consequences because he left the wrench under the car. It's not fair, it's not logical, and I amplify all that in my mind until I explode. Then, and now. Nothing's changed. Wow."

Nysa smiled. "Boom! All right, let's shift it over to the trash can. Mom puts you in the trash can for something. You didn't wash all the dishes, you were reading instead of chopping wood, whatever, and when she called you out on it, you ran your mouth, told her that all work and no play makes Justin a dull boy. Now you're in the trash can, waiting for your dad to come home and spank you. Your negative cognition is *I feel stupid*. Does that still resonate?"

I visualized myself sitting in the trash can, brooding. *I'm a screw-up, I'm stupid, I can't do anything right.* "Yes, that feels right."

"Okay." She jotted down my answer before continuing. "How do you feel when your mom puts you in the trash? Do you feel like she's throwing you away? Like you're worthless?"

"I don't think I was mad at her—"

"Damnit, Justin! She put you in the trash can!" Nysa's eyes blazed, and I realized she was nearly crying. "That's not okay! I need you to acknowledge that. I don't think you've accepted the fact that you were abused. I want you to say it out loud, right now: *I was abused by my parents.* Say it."

I squirmed. Even now, after talking to her about all these things for weeks, months, I had a difficult time saying it. I could talk about the things they did, but it wasn't like I got burned with cigars or punched in the face by a drunken parent. They were just excessive with their discipline, and emotionally vacant, except for anger. But the fact that Nysa was upset made me wonder if I was blocking something out. She shouldn't be feeling this more than me, right? "I just, you know, lots of other people had it way worse than me," I said weakly.

"You don't have to be the most-abused to qualify. You were physically abused, you were very definitely emotionally abused, and you have to come to terms with that. Everything that you're trying to fix about yourself is based on these experiences. Healthy parents don't give their kids sticks for Christmas. Healthy kids don't grow up sitting inside the dumpster waiting for a beating. You were abused. Think about it. If your neighbor was doing those things to his kid, would you consider it good parenting?"

I shook my head in defeat. "No, you're right. I was abused." Once it was out, I felt better. There was no need for me to protect my parents, especially at my own expense. My dad was sixteen years in his grave, and while my mom was still alive, we didn't talk much. Not admitting the truth to myself wasn't doing either of them any good.

"One more time," Nysa said.

I took a deep breath and let it out. I'd pointedly avoided the idea that I'd been abused most of my life. Just thinking it was enough to make me feel guilty in my younger days, and so I just didn't acknowledge it at all. Now that I was searching for my truth, it was important for me to admit this to myself, to mean it, to own it. To believe it. "I was abused. My parents abused me."

"Thank you," Nysa said. "I know that was hard, but you have to process that fact if you're going to get past any of the rest of this stuff. We're not putting Band-Aids on things here. We're going to the core problems."

I nodded silently.

"Now then. How did you feel when your mom put you in the trash can?"

I tried to dive deep, pushing past the surface ideas of protecting my parents, past blaming myself, way down to the center of my feelings. Sitting inside the disgusting can, stewing in the stench and the filth, what did I really believe about myself? I believed that I was unwanted. Unloved. Unworthy. It wasn't just my parents who wanted to throw me away. *I* wanted to throw me away. I was no better than the grime-soaked grocery store receipt at the bottom of the can.

"I feel worthless," I said. "I just want to vanish, to cease existing."

"That sounds more like it," Nysa said. "I want you to go back to that day, sitting inside the trash can. You've got your emotional support team, Bob Ross and Dr. Who. I want you to take them inside with you, all right? And outside, you've got your protection team. Gandalf, and who else did you choose?"

"Gandalf, the Iron Druid, and Xena, Warrior Princess," I said. It had taken me a while to come up with a team of heroes who shared my values, and I was proud of my roster. Team Justin wasn't filled with flashy action stars, but it was a group of people who could get me through any situation without sacrificing the things I held important.

She nodded. "That's right. They're standing around the outside of the trash can, protecting you. No one can get past them, not your mom, not your dad, no one. I want you to find that little black box of feelings that you've got locked away inside and crack the lid open. You don't have to let them all out if you don't want to, but we need to see what's in that box."

I closed my eyes. The image of Gandalf and the others standing in front of a filthy green dumpster, protecting the little blonde eight-year-old boy inside was so distressing that I was crying before I even realized it. The scene was so peaceful at first glance, my mom sitting at her sewing machine on the other side of the porch, and the washing machine running beside the deep freeze, all so very domestic. But the big trash can, out of place in the middle of floor, subtly exposed the underlying sickness, the horror of the emotionally-damaged woman who was making a beautiful yellow dress while simultaneously destroying her child's will to live. The violent duality of the image overwhelmed me with grief. It hurt to cry, physically, both in my face and in my chest, but I let the tears come anyway. I imagined Bob Ross putting a hand on my shoulder as Dr. Who pulled me into a sideways hug.

From an outside perspective, looking in the window of the back porch, I couldn't even pretend that the little boy in the trash can was to blame for the situation. The very idea that he had forced things to come to this was absurd. Xena, standing there with her hand on her sword, ready to protect the boy, really helped put it in perspective for me. The parents were broken, not the child. I wept for myself, for all those years I thought it had been my fault. I wept for the boy in the trash can, and I wept for my adult self, the one still trying to sort everything out.

When my tears slowed, I put myself inside the trash can, becoming eight once again. The paddles buzzing in my hands faded to the background as I settled into place. The confining walls around me left little room to spare, but Bob Ross and Dr. Who were both right there with me, one on either side.

I opened my child eyes. It was dim inside the trash can, but not dark. The splotches and stains on the wall in front of me were visible, along with bits of paper and various wrappers glued to the sticky spots. The smell of fetid garbage washed over me. I quickly moved past that to my other senses, the sound of the washing machine going through the rinse cycle beside me, the vibration coming through the wooden floor, the sweat on the back of my neck from the heat of a summer afternoon in Oklahoma. Having arrived fully in the moment, I searched for the secret box, the one with chains and locks and ropes and hexes and wards preventing it from ever being opened: the box of feelings.

I located the box in a hidden recess in my chest, a place that had always been there but was never observed. It wasn't actually a box at all, not when I was finally able to look directly at it. Beneath the projected façade of a locked chest, it was really a dark sphere. The incredible weight of it, despite the relatively small size, helped me understand what it was: a black hole. I had been unconsciously jamming feelings and memories into it for so long that it had the mass and density of a planet that was compressed to the size of a bowling ball. The thought of opening it up and letting something out was absolutely terrifying. Dr. Who grabbed my hand and held it tight as we stared at the swirling black mass of raw feelings.

"What's coming up?" Nysa's voice came from far away, familiar, yet strange.

Now that I'd found it, I struggled to break free from the gravity of the black hole. What if I'd gotten too close? Was that how people get trapped in their own minds? A jolt of panic shot through me, spurring me back to reality, and I opened my eyes with relief. The paddles were silent and still in my hands, and my beard was soaked with unwiped tears.

"I found my box of feelings," I said, clearing my throat.

"Did you open it?"

I shook my head. "I'm afraid of what's in there," I whispered.

"Why are you afraid?"

I swiped at my cheek with my shoulder, unwilling to look at her. "Because there's so much there. So much. It's a black hole." I took my glasses off and buried my face in my hands as I began to cry again. It didn't hurt so bad this time, and that was a relief. Still, I had so little practice at crying that I didn't really know what to do with it. I kept my face in my hands and let it come.

"It's okay," Nysa said. "It's okay to feel what you're feeling. You're not going through this alone."

I nodded, grateful that she was with me, but I couldn't answer. At some point it occurred to me that if I was feeling all this, then I must have pulled some things from the black hole. The tears were my way of releasing the pent-up pain, and the more I let them flow, the better I felt. It made sense, in a way. There's far more room outside than there is inside, especially for something that never stops growing. When the moment was over, I blew my nose, wiped my eyes, and put my glasses back on. "Okay, I guess I did release some stuff. But I'm glad I did. I feel way better. Kind of."

"I knew you would," Nysa said with a smile. "What else did you think about besides the black hole of feelings?"

I'd almost forgotten my breakthrough. "Oh, yeah! I finally realized that it's a little ridiculous to blame myself for ending up in the trash can. I just had to get some perspective on the situation, to see it from outside myself. That really did it for me."

"Finally," Nysa said. "I'm glad you got there. What was the new understanding?"

It hurt to say it out loud, much like the admission of abuse, but I made myself do it. These were the things that were keeping me from becoming the person I wanted to be. I had to acknowledge them to someone else, to get it outside myself and let it go, or I would never evolve into my best self. "My mother was sick, even sicker than my dad. She filled my head with ideas about myself that weren't true. It doesn't matter if she meant to hurt me or not— it happened. But it wasn't about me. It was never about me. She was the one who was damaged and flawed, not me. I'm starting to sense a pattern here."

Nysa wrote for a moment, a faint smile on her face. When she finished, she dropped the pen on the desk and folded her hands in her lap. "Your mother *was* sick, Justin. She was hurting, and filled with her own negative thoughts, and you just happened to be there. You're right— it was never about you. No one else was making you feel this way about yourself, right? Not your teachers, not your neighbors, not the people at church. Just your primary caregivers. The two people who were supposed to protect you, and love you, and teach you how to be a whole person. But they weren't able to do that for you because they were sick, they were broken, and they were in pain. You understand that now."

"I do," I said. "I really do."

"And look at yourself," she went on. "You endured all of that, and you still made it to this point. You screamed through the pain and tried to find a way to make it stop. Some of the things you tried didn't work, or hurt you even more, but eventually, you found something that *will* help. You made it to a place where you can regroup and change directions. The fact that you're here is a testament to your ability to overcome. A testament to your resilience, your strength, your character. You're trying to break the cycle."

I fidgeted from the discomfort that suddenly enveloped me. "I don't know what to say to that. It feels a little arrogant to pat myself on the back."

Nysa shook her head. "It's arrogant if you start thinking you're better than everyone else because of it. It's honest self-assessment if you use it to prove to yourself that you have value, and that you aren't all of those negative things you thought about yourself."

"Okay, that makes sense," I said. "And I *do* need to acknowledge those things. You're right. They're true. I'll work on that."

"We'll get there. For now, let's go ahead and put all this stuff in your Pensieve. Put the trash can in there, the wrenches, everything. It'll be safe there, and you can pull bits and pieces of it back out if you want to work on it between now and our next session. If you want to leave it all in there, that's fine, too."

I imagined putting everything we had talked about inside a big box. My Pensieve, the mysterious silver bowl filled with my thoughts and memories, was really a portal to my own mental universe. I went through the fog on top and plunged into the blackness of space, flying past dozens of stars until I reached the one I was looking for, a huge blue giant. There, on the second planet out, I flew down to a city, eventually landing inside a massive storage complex. I rolled open the door to an unmarked stall, set the box on the floor, and closed the unit. There was no need to lock it here. Everything in this storage facility belonged to me, and there was no one else on the planet to mess with it, anyway.

Eight-year-old Justin needed a place to go, too. There was no way I was leaving him to sit in the trash can forever. I'd loved adventure stories when I was that age, so I took him to an island on another planet in that same star system and introduced him to the Swiss Family Robinson. There, he would be able to run across swinging bridges and climb trees, and no harm would come to him. I smiled as he looked around, his eyes filled with joy and excitement. "Go on," I whispered to him. "Have fun. Be yourself. It's okay."

I opened my eyes, back in Nysa's office. "Done."

"That was a really good session," she said. "You made a lot of progress today. How do you feel?"

"Exhausted." I smiled weakly. "Mentally, emotionally, physically exhausted. But in a good way."

It felt strange to think positively about myself as a kid. My brain was working overtime to keep up with the new developments, and I had a long way to go to work out all my other issues, but I was elated about the progress I was making. There was light at the end of the tunnel, and it wasn't a train coming at me. I had hope, and more than that, I had proof that I could change the way I felt. I was reinventing myself, becoming my true self, and finally, I could see myself as someone I wanted to be. What an incredible gift!

Chapter 5

Nysa scrubbed the paddles with a disinfecting wipe. Somehow, she managed to sit in an office chair as if it were a couch. I was far too tall to pull that off, and I doubted that my knees could handle it anyway.

"We've really been cruising through your trauma timeline," she said, tossing the paddles to me. "You're making great progress with this stuff."

I smiled, relishing the compliment. Personal growth had become a way of life for me in the years since I got sober, but it wasn't something that others generally commented on. "I have a great guide and a strong desire to change. That helps a lot."

"It does. If you don't want to change, all the therapy in the world won't help you. People come through here all the time, miserable and unwilling to do anything differently."

"It's the human condition," I said. "I'm glad I'm not from this planet. It must be horrible."

"It is for some people," Nysa said, pulling the accordion arm of the lamp across her desk so the light was on the paperwork. "Let's see. The next thing on your list is *Mom and Dad invading my church*. What's that about?"

I cast about for a way to condense ten years of experiences and feelings into a few sentences. It wasn't easy. My mother was still on the early side of her religious mania back then. It was brewing, as her views on non-Christian music showed, but she wasn't displaying blatant symptoms that I recognized then. Those came later.

"My folks went to the same church all of my childhood, as far back as I can remember. It was a big building, two-story with a basement, five or six hundred people, although the auditorium could easily hold a thousand. We never missed a service, Sunday morning, Sunday night, Wednesday night. My mom always had to sit in the second row even though we were perpetually late, so we had to parade past everyone there, and I felt embarrassed about that."

"I guess it didn't embarrass them too much, huh?" Nysa said.

"I don't think they were capable of being embarrassed," I said. "I remember the one time I got to sit with someone else during church, one of the kids from my Sunday School class. Somehow my dad noticed from halfway across this giant auditorium that I wasn't paying attention to the sermon. He got up and walked over there, shuffling past everyone on the pew. He grabbed me by the ear and dragged me out to the hallway and whipped my ass, then dragged me down to the front row to sit with them. I was humiliated beyond description, of course, and I never sat with anyone else again."

Nysa looked at me intently. "It's interesting that he would do that. I wonder what he got out of it. A sense of power? *See how tough I am,* or *See what a strict parent I am,* or something, maybe. Interesting."

I had never thought about my dad's perspective in those situations. The idea of getting up in front of five hundred people and making such a scene would be unthinkable for me, and probably for most people. What had been going through his mind? I hadn't been making noise or distracting others. I'd just been bored with the service, as most kids probably were, and for once, I had someone to pass notes back and forth with, as opposed to daydreaming about whatever book I was reading at the time.

"I don't know what he was thinking," I said. "It never occurred to me to wonder. See how self-centered I am?" I flashed a smile to let her know I was joking.

"All right, back on track."

"Sorry, rabbit hole. Anyway, I knew the Bible backwards and forwards by the time I was seven or eight, and I was baptized when I was nine. They had me up there leading singing on Sunday nights, and I even wrote a few sermons and preached them as part of the youth program. I had to stand on a stool to see over the pulpit. I didn't know back then that you could go to church and not be 100% committed to everything. All I knew was my mom and dad were always the very last ones to leave, and that I had to do all the stuff to avoid going to Hell."

"So were you doing it to avoid punishment?"

"Not at first, no. I didn't start questioning the dogma until I was ten or eleven. Before that, I believed everything they told me. I thought everyone except the people who went to that particular church was going to Hell, and I was all for praising Jesus. It took me a while to apply logic to the Bible. I didn't think I was supposed to question things, right? Just like I couldn't question my dad. Same concept.

"Anyway, that church was in Bartlesville. We moved to Dewey, the next town over, when I was six, and even though there was a branch of that church three blocks from our new house, we kept going to the same one in Bartlesville. When I was twelve and really getting desperate to escape from my family, I convinced them to let me start going to the church in Dewey. I don't know how I was successful, but somehow they relented and let me switch. I think part of it was that the youth minister in Bartlesville quit right before I was old enough to join the youth group. Mom said he went off to sell pornography, although I later found out that he worked at a movie rental place, like Blockbuster or something. To my mom, the fact that they carried adult movies essentially made him a Satan worshiper, and she was sure he had been corrupting the children of Bartlesville all that time. Panic about Satan worship was a big thing in the '80's."

I stretched my legs out, trying to remember that time. The Dewey church was right next to my school, and I walked by it every day. It was much smaller than the church in Bartlesville, but it was an interesting building, an A-frame design with a steep roof that went all the way to the ground. I wasn't looking for a place to grow spiritually, as I'd already lost interest in religion by then, but I was very interested in creating a new peer group away from my family. I was an outcast at school, and I didn't really have any friends at the church in Bartlesville, and I felt that my parents were largely responsible for that. This was a way for me to start over in a place where I was a relative stranger.

"By switching churches, I was hoping to get out of my parents' shadow. I needed a do-over, and that was the only way I could think of to make it happen. We'd been to the church in Dewey a few times before for special events, and I knew that no one from my class at school went there. It was perfect."

"You wanted to reinvent yourself," Nysa said. "And you figured out a way to make it happen. That's pretty impressive for a twelve-year-old kid."

I shrugged. "Well, it worked great for a little while. The youth group was awesome. They accepted me for me, loved me, included me, everything I had been missing out on my whole life. It was fantastic. And it wasn't just the kids. It was their parents, too, and the youth minister. I was part of something that made me feel good about me. That was a really big deal."

The memories came flooding back, things I hadn't thought about in many years. Sunday nights after church, we would go to someone's house for snacks and devotional time. That was what I lived for. Chips and soda, cookies, sandwiches, which all seemed like ridiculous luxuries to me, as we never had anything like that at my house. Camaraderie, with jokes and games and laughing. Girls, with whom I was deeply in love, who, while not necessarily returning my romantic affection, didn't turn a cold shoulder to me, and even let me sit next to them on the couch, our legs touching. Holding hands with them during the prayer. Big things for a thirteen-year-old boy who'd never had a girlfriend.

Van rides to events in Tulsa were another thing I loved. One such trip was to a concert. We went to see Michael W. Smith, a Christian rock legend at that time. Someone else paid for my ticket, of course, as my parents never had a dime to spare. We all brought a sack lunch to eat on the way. Mine was a can of refried beans dumped into a Tupperware container, compliments of my mother. *It's all we can afford to give you. You're lucky to be going at all, so don't complain, or you'll stay home.* I was embarrassed about my food, as everyone else had ham sandwiches and bags of chips, carrot sticks and candy bars. The second I cracked the lid on my beans, the overwhelming scent of garlic filled the van, followed immediately by a chorus of groans and pretend gagging. I put the lid back on, my face so hot that I could feel the tips of my ears burning and pulsing. One of the other boys saw me sliding my beans under the seat and gave me half of his sandwich. I thanked him quietly, resisting the overwhelming urge to hug him. The sandwich was delicious. I wished I lived at his house.

"So, what happened?" Nysa asked. "Obviously, your parents brought the roof crashing down somehow."

"I don't know what it was specifically. My mom had a falling out with the Bartlesville church, some difference of opinion on a scripture, I'm sure. Or maybe God wasn't solving her problems the way she was hoping, and she blamed it on the church. That became her M.O. in later years, so this might have been an early occurrence. I think she had already jumped off the high dive by then, but I didn't realize it until she quit the church in Bartlesville and switched to mine in Dewey.

"Aside from the horror of my parents unexpectedly invading my sanctuary, there was also the shock of my mother pronouncing the church in Bartlesville as doing all sorts of things wrong, and not following the word of God, etc. That was a complete role reversal, the first of many to come, but that was the first. It was as if everything she had told me to be gospel, or fact, she was suddenly taking back and changing her mind on. That event shattered the glass bubble around my belief of *The World According to My Mom.* I didn't know what to trust anymore. It was a weird dichotomy in my head. Even though I hated being associated with them, I still operated on the assumption that they were right about things, and everyone else was wrong. For her to change her mind about something so big and important just blew me away."

"Your trust in her infallibility was destroyed," Nysa said.

"Exactly. And then, at the same time that was happening, they were barging into my church."

"And what was your fear with that?"

"That …" I took a deep breath and let it out. "That people would get to know them and realize how crazy and weird they were, and that they would reject me based on that. That if people, I guess my youth group, mostly, realized what my family was like, they'd think differently of me. How could they not?"

"You were afraid of losing status, being found out as a fraud?"

"Yeah, exactly," I said. "It was as if my identity relied on no one in my youth group ever meeting anyone who knew me in any other capacity. Someone from my class at school coming in who knew I was an outcast nerd would have been bad. My parents showing up was absolutely devastating."

"What was it about them that people would see as weird that would change their opinion of you?"

The list of answers that formed in my head was a scroll that dropped to the ground and unwound for ages, mile after mile. I found the visual amusing, but not enough to bring the smile in my head to my lips. The negative weight of the things on that list was too heavy to allow that.

"To put it all into context, you have to remember that I was an outsider all my life. I didn't feel like part of my family, and I wasn't accepted by the other kids at school, especially as I got older. My childhood friend from down the street didn't even hang out with me anymore, and it was because my parents were strange. So, all I wanted to be was normal, to fit in. Make sense?"

Nysa nodded.

"By this time, my mom had discovered historical reenactment. They were part of this club that did pre-1840 mountain man and Indian rendezvous, which was essentially primitive camping, wearing costumes, shooting black-powder rifles, and all that. My folks went overboard with it, of course, because that's what they do. My dad had long hair that he braided, like Willie Nelson, and a big black bushy beard. He looked like a biker, but he wasn't. He was a mountain man blacksmith. My mom, the seamstress, made all of his shirts, as well as her dresses and clothes for my sister and brother, and they were pre-1840's style. Think *Pocahontas* meets *Gone with the Wind.* Not hideous, just very, very different. And she was getting into her Cherokee medicine woman phase then, so she had the leather medicine bag hanging around her neck and everything. They stuck out like crazy in a church filled with suits and ties. And they sat in the front, can't forget that. The youth group sat in the center row, second pew. That was our spot. Suddenly, my family was in the next row over, looking like they'd just walked off the set of *Little House on the Prairie.* It was like getting hit by a bus, every week."

Nysa was writing notes on her sheet. "Did you get ostracized by your youth group?"

I didn't have a clear answer to that right away. The feeling of intense shame was a constant companion, especially when they first started coming. That's what I was feeling, but I didn't know what the others were actually thinking. I spent a lot of time and effort making sure that everyone knew that the only thing I had in common with those people was my address, and that I was being held against my will. Whether I was successful in that or not wasn't something I was conscious of. I just kept working it, trying to create separation from them.

"I remember feeling like an outcast, but in retrospect, I don't think that much of anything changed. I was still part of the group. One of my friends and his dad would take me out shooting or fishing sometimes, and that didn't change. I felt a bit on the outside right up to the end, but I really wasn't. I think it was just me feeling self-conscious."

"What was the end?"

There was no reason for me to be nervous about telling her this story, but I still felt awkward. Steeling my nerves, I pressed forward. "This is a rabbit hole, but it's an important one."

Nysa laughed. "Of course it's a rabbit hole. Everything here is a rabbit hole. Most of them are filled with false feelings and memories, and we're clearing them out. That's the whole point of therapy!"

"All right, all right," I said. "Fair enough. So, my mom and dad were big into this historical reenactment thing, right? And somewhere along the line, my mom decided that she was a Cherokee medicine woman. In her head, she managed to merge that with her intense Christianity. Anyway, she read some books by an actual Native American, and decided that the apocalypse was coming. Like, end of the world stuff. The only survivors would be the people in this commune in Colorado, who would start civilization over again."

"This is what the book said?" Nysa asked.

I shrugged. "I don't think it said it directly, but I never read the books. My mom said it was written in code so that only the chosen ones would get the message."

"And she was chosen, of course," Nysa said sardonically. "So, what happened?"

"We sold all of our stuff, along with another family that believed my mom, and we loaded what was left in a big trailer and got ready to go to Colorado. The idea of leaving my youth group was devastating. Somehow that was far worse for me than the fact that my mom had completely lost her mind. It was supposed to be a big secret, but one Sunday night at our devotional, we were all sitting in a big circle, and I broke down and told everyone what was happening. I told them the truth, that the story my parents were telling about moving for a new job was a lie, that my mom had lost her mind and thought the world was ending."

Nysa was staring at me spellbound. "How did they take it?"

"Everyone agreed that my parents were crazy. It wasn't much of a leap for them, though. They saw how my parents showed up to church. The youth minister and the parents there had a huddle in the kitchen, and ten minutes later they pulled me off to the side while everyone else went back to singing songs."

I closed my eyes, and instantly I was there. We were at the Cooper's house, a clean brick ranch with nice furnishings, the kind of place I dreamed about living. Everything was decorated with sunflowers. The flour pot on the counter, the towel hanging from the stove handle, the cover on the mixer. The youth minister and his wife were there, along with Mr. and Mrs. Davis, and the Coopers.

"Justin, is this really happening?" That was Jeff, the youth minister. "It sounds pretty far out there."

I nodded miserably, ashamed, and regretting opening my mouth in the first place. I should have just gone on with the charade and let them all think my dad had a great new job somewhere. Now I was going to be banished in shame.

Mrs. Davis stepped forward and wrapped her arms around me, pulling me into a tight hug. "We're not going to let this happen to you," she said, releasing me. "Steve and I are willing to adopt you. You can come live with us. You don't have to go."

Too stunned to speak, I looked at her, then at the others in the circle. Hands reached out and grabbed my shoulders in support. My vision blurred, and my throat locked up. I had no idea what to say, anyway. Flashes of a life that could be raced through my mind. A loving, supportive family, new clothes, good food, it all seemed wonderful. I felt undeserving of such an offer.

"Holy crap, Justin." Nysa's voice cut through the memory. "That's about the ultimate form of acceptance, huh? They were willing to bring you into their home and raise you with their kids? That's huge! People don't just casually do that."

Her outsider's perspective opened my eyes to something I'd somehow never grasped, and the insight exploded in my mind. "I don't think I ever realized it before now, but you're right. Nobody was rejecting me. They were pulling me even closer. The only one who thought less of me because of my family was me."

"*Kapow*!" Nysa leaped out of her chair with her fist raised in the air, her face lighting up in a triumphant grin. "*The only one who thought less of me because of my family was me.* That's a huge breakthrough! Let's write that down."

I leaned back, wrestling with this new revelation. The people who mattered the most to me had never rejected me, no matter what my family did. They loved me for who I was, enough to disrupt their whole lives to rescue me. Nysa was right— that was the ultimate acceptance. Mom and Dad invading my church wasn't a defeat. It was a victory, and a big one.

"This changes my whole perception of that time in my life," I said. "I didn't realize what was really happening back then. I was too wrapped up in my own head to see reality."

"That's what EMDR is for. We're going to lock this in, rewrite the memories and put the positive feelings of belonging and acceptance with them, instead of the rejection. They've been miscategorized all this time." Nysa clapped her hands, still grinning. "This is so exciting! But what did you do? I know you went to high school in Wyoming instead of Oklahoma, so you didn't take them up on it, right?"

"I couldn't make a decision on the spot, so I asked them to give me a bit to process everything. We were supposed to be leaving like three days later. I felt guilty as hell about it, and I don't think I slept much. I remember being out in the driveway, helping my dad load the trailer, when Steve and Jeff drove up. They put me on the spot, asked me right there in front of my dad if I wanted to stay. They said I could get in the car with them right then."

I closed my eyes, feeling the intensity of my dad's anger. He stood at the door of the trailer, loading boxes inside. Steve and Jeff stood to the right of the door, and I was handing boxes from the pile up to my dad. I was absolutely terrified. My dad's iron will pressed down on me like an incredible weight, and I was helpless to resist it. I don't know what I thought he'd do if I left, but it didn't feel possible for me to try. Even with two grown men there ready to rescue me, to take me away to permanent safety— no more insanity, no more rage, no more crazy workload, no more fighting, the answer to all my prayers— I couldn't do it.

"I can't go with you," I whispered hoarsely. "I… I changed my mind."

My dad never even acknowledged them. He stared at me as he held his hands out for the next box, sheer brute dominance controlling me like a puppet master. I knew I was broken, beaten, when I turned and picked it up and handed it to him. Steve and Jeff waited for a moment, watching me. I was crying silently, and I couldn't look at them. I turned and grabbed another box, thrusting it at my dad, then another, and another. At some point, Steve and Jeff were gone, and I felt empty. Even the surety of the coming response from my dad couldn't make me feel any worse than I did in that moment.

"How did your dad handle that?" Nysa asked softly. "After they were gone."

"He never said anything at all. It was like it didn't happen."

"Did you regret not going with Steve and Jeff?"

I nodded. "I did, at least for a while. But it passed. For all the insanity driving the situation, I was still on an adventure, in a way. Some of it was exciting."

"So you went to Colorado," Nysa said. "Obviously the world didn't end. What happened when you got there?"

"It took weeks to get there, for starters. The trailer was way too heavy, and the van broke down a few times. We camped out in state parks for days at a time, and that was kind of cool. But once we got to the place in Colorado, it all fell apart. My mom looked the author up in the phone book and contacted her. She told my mom that it was a fiction book, and that my mom needed to get some therapy."

"And that was it? End of the quest?"

"Pretty much. The other family went back to Oklahoma. We went north until we ran out of gas money. We'd been living on the road for a month by then. My mom found a church and begged for help. They introduced us to the foreman of a cattle outfit, and that's how we ended up on a ranch in Wyoming."

"Back to the church."

"Back to the church," I agreed.

"That must have been pretty devastating for your mom."

I never really thought about how she felt, but she must have been consumed by shame. It wasn't just our lives that she'd turned upside down. The family that had come with us had given up everything, too. They'd pulled their three children from school and cut ties with everyone they'd ever known, assuming they'd never see any of them again. My mother had been playing the role of a prophet, and it had all fallen apart in her hands.

"I think it probably destroyed her, in some ways. I was wrapped up in my own experience then, and I was never aware that either of my parents was capable of experiencing regret or feeling bad about their behavior. And the medicine woman thing sort of faded away when we got to Wyoming. I was in a new school and busy reinventing myself, so I didn't give it much thought, but maybe that whole thing burst her bubble. Then again, it might have yanked the whole rug out from under her feet, because her suicide attempt was only a year or two after that. It never occurred to me that the false apocalypse might have played a part in that, but it seems like it had to be a factor, right?"

Nysa shrugged. "Probably. But bringing it back to you, let's lock in your new perspective on being accepted."

I took a deep breath and closed my eyes. This session had been intense. My whole life had been spent with the knowledge that I'd been an outsider, rejected by all. To realize that I'd been wrong about that, blind to the fact that the people I loved the most had loved me back, was a lot to grasp. But it was true, and I felt good about myself in a way that was foreign to me, an unknown comfort. I leaned into that feeling. It was something I wanted to get used to.

Chapter 6

I WALKED INTO THE STRANGE BUILDING, double-checking the address and suite number against the text message Nysa had sent me. She had been packing up her things on my last visit, and I was excited for her move to a new office space. If I've learned anything in life, it's that change is often good, and I look forward to it. It's also inevitable, and trying to avoid change is far more stressful than accepting it, at least for me.

She met me in the waiting room, a huge grin on her face. "You found it!"

"I did!" I returned her infectious smile. "Are you all settled in already?"

"It's getting there," she said, waving me down the hall as she turned around. "I'm still trying to find the right art to hang since I have these huge walls now, but it's coming together. Come on in."

I followed her into the office. The familiar chair was there, which I was glad to see, as was the abstract motorcycle art. Everything else was new. This room was three times the size of her old office. She now had a small couch and a bigger desk. The most exciting addition, however, at least for me, was the black German Shepherd sitting on a big dog bed under the window at the far end of the room. It wore the bright yellow vest of a service dog.

"You've got space for your dog! That's exciting!" I stayed by the chair, trying to be mindful of her status as a working dog and the rules that go with that, but I really wanted to pet it. Nysa and I had talked about the dog before, and I knew it was important to her.

"I know, right? She's good for me, but it seems like she's good for my clients, too."

"What's her name?"

"Cerby. Short for Cerberus. It's a mythological three-headed guard dog."

"I like it!" Cerby wandered over and sniffed my foot. "Is it okay to pet her? If it's not, that's fine, too."

Nysa chuckled at my awkwardness. "No, it's fine. She's very friendly. The hard part is getting her to leave you alone once you start paying attention to her."

I gave Cerby a scratch on the head, and while her nose stayed glued to my foot, her tail began to wag. "My shoes probably smell like cats, dogs, sheep, donkeys, and horses. She's going to spend the whole hour trying to figure out what all those smells are." She turned to the side, moving my hand down her back, and I laughed. "She knows how to work a crowd."

Nysa gave it a minute as she settled onto the couch and arranged her notes, then sent Cerby back across the room. "Cerby. Bed." The dog immediately moved away, though she stopped halfway across the floor and looked back. Nysa's finger shot out, pointing at the window. "Bed."

Cerby looked dejected but went to her bed and lay down.

"All right, let's see." Nysa shuffled through her notes. "Perfectionism. You've got this on your list. You said you know that you hold yourself and others to impossible standards, but you can't seem to overcome it."

I nodded.

"Give me an example."

"If I take a test, and I get ninety-nine questions right and one question wrong, I'll focus on the one that I got wrong. I probably give it just as much weight as the ninety-nine that I got right, so in my head, I got a fifty-fifty. Does that make sense?"

"Sure."

"Intellectually, I know I'm not giving myself enough credit for the things I do right and way too much blame for the things I do wrong. I know that, but I don't usually recognize that I'm doing it. Not right away, anyway. Once I'm in the depths of despair, I usually figure it out at some point, but I would love to not go there in the first place."

Nysa swung the paddles over to me and plugged them into the controller. "Let's process it. What's your negative cognition?"

Despite having gone through this process countless times, I never seemed to have an answer ready for that question. "Well, there's the obvious surface things, like *I'm not good enough*, but that doesn't quite feel right. I think it's more complicated than that."

"Okay, give me a different example. Be more specific."

I stretched my legs out and pushed the back of the chair into a reclined position, taking a deep breath and letting it out as I got comfortable. "I guess the driveway might be an example. Our driveway is a dirt road, and it's a half mile long. It gets potholes in it, and sometimes I have to go get a truckload of lime rock and shovel it into the holes to smooth the road out. It's a lot of physical labor, and I spend a lot of time packing it in and making it smooth. But later, when I ride down the driveway with Erica, all I notice are the rough spots I missed, and I'm embarrassed about it."

"Does Erica point them out, or say anything?"

"No, of course not. She's never critical of my efforts. And really, she probably doesn't even notice half the stuff I do like that. Like trimming tree branches back off the fence line, or filling in potholes, or cleaning cobwebs out of the barn. Those things are invisible unless you point them out, and I try not to point them out to her. Well, sometimes. Sometimes I need her to know how hard I worked."

"Why is it bad to tell her what you did?"

"Because I'm not supposed to seek external validation. I'm trying to stop doing that and work more towards giving myself credit for what I do."

"That's good to a degree, but there's nothing wrong with showing your wife what you did. And because I know your love language is *acts of service*, I know that you do most of those things for her. And if you're doing them for her, and she's not likely to realize it on her own because of the nature of the things you're doing, you have to show her. That's completely different than telling everyone you know about how you trimmed the trees or fixed the driveway. Do you see the difference?"

"Yeah, I can see that."

"Now, the relevant part for this discussion is that when you show her what you did, she sees the smooth road, or the nice fence, and you see the bump you missed, or a tree branch hanging lower than the others."

"Right."

"Okay, we're getting somewhere. Let's go back to your childhood. What's the earliest time you can remember this kind of thinking?"

I closed my eyes and let my thoughts wander. The firewood stack came to mind, but the expectation of perfection was from my dad, not me. The same with fetching wrenches. As I thought about other events, I realized they were all like that. I opened my eyes. "Am I looking for times when I expected myself to be perfect? Because I have a lot of things where my dad expected me to be perfect, and I have a feeling that's probably what started all this."

Nysa flashed a dark smile. "Ya think?"

"Of course it is," I muttered. "What else would it be?"

"Let's find a time when you did something, and your dad pointed out the flaws and ignored the parts you did well." She shuffled through her notes. "This sounds really familiar, like we've already talked about it."

"Stacking the firewood," I said. "Me getting a swat for each piece that was out of line. But we used it for a different cognition."

"That's right. Find a different one for me."

I settled back into the chair and closed my eyes again. My childhood was filled with hard work and big projects, and the timeline was fuzzy. There was the lumber pile. My dad had gotten a bunch of used lumber from someone who had torn a house down. His plan was to use it to build a second story onto our house. That project eventually happened, but first it was my job to remove the nails from the lumber. Thousands and thousands of nails, and I couldn't miss one, because if my dad had to cut a board and the saw hit a nail, it could break the blade. It took me months of working every day after school. When my dad came home, he would count how many boards I'd completed, check them for missed nails, and check the ground for any dropped nails. Each missed or dropped nail was a swat, of course. That was always the deal.

Before that, though, was the water line project. My dad decided to replace the main water pipe that came off the city line and into the house. Or maybe he was running another water pipe to a new location. I don't remember the specifics, or maybe I never knew. My dad wasn't big on explaining why we did things. I was just supposed to keep my mouth shut and do as I was told.

"I think the water line project was one of the early ones. We were replacing the water line going into the house, and I had to dig the ditch for it."

"How old were you?"

"Maybe eight? Ten? I'm not positive. I know I was in elementary school, and it was before we built on the second story, which was also in elementary school, so yeah. We'll say eight."

"Tell me about the ditch project. What was the expectation?"

"My dad drove a wooden stake in the ground at each end and tied a string between them. I had to dig a ditch under the string. It had to be the depth of the spade, which was probably about eighteen inches, and it had to be perfectly straight under the string. Dirt was to be off to one side, all on the same side. It couldn't be close enough to fall back in the ditch, but no further away than absolutely necessary."

"How far did you have to go?"

I tried to picture the yard. Everything seemed so much bigger then, and it was hard to know real distances. "The city water pipe came through our back yard. Our line came off of it and ran up the side of the house about three quarters of the way to the front. Maybe fifty or sixty feet?"

"Okay, I want you to go back there to eight-year-old Justin. You've got the spade, and the string, and sixty feet of deep ditch to dig. Go there, get in the moment." She turned on the paddles.

It was 1984, and I was standing beside the house with the spade. It was shorter than the regular shovel, which made it less unwieldy for me at that age. All I had to do was dig right under the string, which should be easy. A feeling of excitement surged through me, and I was confident that with a different shovel, one more my size, I would be able to dig a great ditch. My dad was going to be so impressed! For once, I had a task that I could complete with ease. This time everything was going to be different.

I looked around the yard. The birdbath was there, near the back of the house. It was a big, heavy concrete thing, but for some reason, the top was never on the pedestal. It sat on its side against a tree for all of my memory. The base stood nearby, a three-foot concrete column with six inches of pipe sticking out of the top. I remembered draping myself across the column, the pipe pressing painfully into my stomach, and carefully lifting my feet up in the air, wondering if it would impale me.

"What's coming up?" Nysa shut the paddles off and waited as I collected my thoughts.

"I was mostly getting into the setting," I said. "I was trying to remember what all was in the yard, and I got hung up thinking about the birdbath."

Nysa arched her left eyebrow. "Birdbath? Was there something special about it?"

I shrugged, momentarily debating about whether to go down that rabbit hole or not. "It didn't have the dish on it, so it was just the base with a pipe sticking out of it. Before I learned how to use my dad's revolver, impaling myself on the birdbath was my suicide plan."

Her face softened. "How old were you when you first started

fantasizing about suicide?"

"Six, I guess. Not long after my sister was born."

"That's young. Did you ever try back then?"

"Not seriously, no. I used to get up on the birdbath and lay on the pipe, just testing it out. I knew I'd have to jump down on it from the tree to actually do it, which I never did, but I would feel it out sometimes. Mainly I just liked imagining how horrible my parents would feel. I learned to be passive aggressive pretty early on. The six-year-old martyr."

Nysa wrote for another minute before putting her pen down. "All right, back to the ditch. We'll revisit the birdbath another time, but I want to stay on track with this. Ready?"

I nodded, and she flipped the switch on the paddles. I closed my eyes and embraced the buzzing, left, right, left, right. This time the ditch was in progress, and the frustrations were evident. The biggest problem I faced was tree roots. What I thought would be an easy dig was actually a nightmare of trying to hack through endless roots of varying sizes. This slowed me down tremendously, and it also made it difficult to clear the dirt out of the ditch. The protruding roots that I'd already cut would grab the edges of the spade and cause most of the dirt to fall back in. Two steps forward, one step back.

Another problem was the string. I was supposed to be digging directly beneath it to keep the ditch straight, but it kept getting in the way. My legs got tangled in it, the spade got tangled in it, and more than once I'd had to go pound the stakes back in the ground. I had no way to keep the ditch straight without the string, but I couldn't dig with the string in place. My early optimism of pleasing my dad had turned into despair at yet another impossible situation.

The paddles stopped buzzing, and I opened my eyes. Nysa was looking at me expectantly.

"I'd forgotten what a disaster that was."

"In what way?"

"In every way. I was supposed to dig a certain amount every day before my dad got home from work, but the tree roots slowed me down so bad there was no way I could get it done. It was also impossible for me to get the ditch as pretty and clean as he wanted it, also because of the tree roots."

"What were you feeling?"

I let out a breath, trying to feel everything from that moment. "I was frustrated. I couldn't do what I was supposed to do. There was no way to win. No matter what I tried, I was going to get a spanking when my dad got home. I hated that helpless feeling. And he never said anything supportive about what I did manage to get done. I was working my ass off, and he never even acknowledged that part."

"And where do you feel that?"

"In my gut. Queasy stomach. It's always my stomach."

Nysa picked up her pen and notepad. "Okay. You had a difficult task that you were capable of completing, but not within the parameters he put on it. You felt helpless, because you were going to be punished for not meeting an impossible expectation, and there were no excuses accepted. You also felt like your efforts weren't appreciated. Is that right?"

"That's pretty much it."

"High work, high punishment, no approval. What do you think for a negative cognition? I'm not good enough? I'm invisible? No one cares about me?"

They all felt right, in a way. My dad treated me the same way he would treat a machine. Program it to do a task, get mad at it if it failed. It wasn't even that he didn't care about me— it was more like he didn't even realize that I might have feelings at all. I really was invisible to him and my mother in many ways. "I'm invisible. I think that rings true the most."

Nysa nodded, writing it down. "And our positive cognition? Remember, it doesn't just have to be the opposite of the negative. How do you want to feel in that situation?"

"I want to …" If all the conditions were the same, but I could feel differently about myself in that moment, what did I want to feel? "I want to feel like I *can* do it. I want to feel capable, instead of like a helpless victim."

"*I am capable.*" Nysa looked up from her notes. "I think that's good. Let's rate it and do some processing. On a scale of one to ten, and paired with the impossible ditch, how disturbing is it to say, *I am invisible*?"

My stomach churned as I immersed myself in the feelings. "Ten."

"And on a scale of one to seven, paired with the ditch, how true does it feel to say, *I am capable*?"

"One."

"Okay, here we go."

The paddles began buzzing in my hands, left, right, left, right. I stabbed the spade into the ground as far as it would go, then stood on the top of the blade. The metal dug through the soles of my cheap tennis shoes as I jumped up and down, trying to maximize the impact of my meager body weight. The arches of my feet were bruised and sore, but I had no other way to get it done.

I am invisible. Looking up at the ditch I'd completed so far was depressing, although I was over the halfway point. Despite the guide string, the trench weaved in a drunken line, wider in some spots than others due to the roots I'd had to hack out. It represented more than a week of my after-school life, as well as a weekend. Two sore feet. Eight whippings. Thirty feet of ditch dug. Thirty feet to go. I'd always been good at math, so I could project eight more whippings to go, maybe nine. I didn't dwell on that part, because I got a whipping every day for something. Finishing the ditch wasn't going to make that go away.

The bottom of the trench could barely be seen through the forest of roots sticking out from the walls. Many were small, skinnier than a pencil, but some were as thick as the shovel handle. At some point I had learned that if I cut the roots near one side wall, rather than in the center, I could then cut them near the other side wall. Sometimes. While that made it a little easier to get the dirt out of the trench, it took longer because I was cutting each root twice. My technique might be getting better but my speed wasn't, and the results were the only thing that mattered to my dad.

I am invisible. If I were dead, my dad would have to finish digging this ditch himself. Would he realize how hard I had been working if he was fighting with these roots? Would his feet be sore? Probably not. He was so much stronger than me, and his heavy work boots would protect his feet. He could probably dig this whole ditch in a day or two. What would it take for him to appreciate how hard I worked, even if I wasn't perfect?

What would it take … what would it take for him to appreciate me? My eyes popped open, and Nysa turned off the paddles with a questioning smile.

"Well, that looked like an insight."

I nodded. "I was thinking about what it would take for my dad to appreciate the effort I was making. Like, if I killed myself and he had to dig the rest of the ditch himself, would that be enough to get his attention? And that's when I realized he wasn't ever going to acknowledge my effort. He never even thought about my effort. It wasn't on his radar."

"Did you ever talk to your mom about your feelings?"

"Sometimes. If it was a good day, she'd tell me that Dad appreciated how hard I worked, but he wasn't very good at saying it. If it was a bad day, she'd hear me out, and then at supper she'd explain to my dad how instead of working, I'd spent the afternoon inside complaining about my chores. Then he'd beat my ass and add more tasks to my list. I never knew how it would go, so I didn't risk it very often."

"She might be a confidant, but you couldn't trust her."

"Right."

"Okay, bring the focus back to your dad. Let's do it again." Nysa flicked the switch, turning the paddles back on.

What was happening for my dad? What was his perspective? He would assign me a task, and then go work on something else. There were a thousand things to be done, and he was trying to work through them. Rightly or wrongly, he expected me to accomplish my tasks to his satisfaction, but it wasn't about me. It was about him driving himself to get all these things done. He would work all day at his job, then come home and work half the night. It wasn't that I was doing a bad job. It was that he had more than he could handle, and it was kicking his ass.

My dad was terminally frustrated with his life, and understandably so. There was never enough money. The house was falling apart, the car was broken down, and his wife was unhinged. It wasn't that he didn't care about my efforts— it's that he never even thought about it. He was wrapped up in his own sense of failure, and he lashed out at me because I was there, a safe target. Otherwise, I really *was* invisible to him. But I wasn't invisible, not really. He was just blinded. I was trying to get a blind man to see what I was doing. It was never going to happen.

When I finished the ditch, it was just going to advance his list of chores to the next item. For me, it was a monumental task, a life test that I had to pass, but for him, it was just one more thing to do. There were no accolades waiting for me, but that didn't mean my efforts were meaningless. It just meant that I had to give myself the pat on the back.

"What's coming up?" Nysa asked, ripping me out of the thought.

"I think I got it," I said. "My dad never acknowledged my effort, but it had nothing to do with me. It was never about me at all. He was dealing with his own endless crises, and just taking it out on me when it didn't come together for him. It wasn't that he thought *I* wasn't good enough, it's that he thought *he* wasn't good enough."

"Yes!" Nysa shouted. "Exactly! You dug the impossible ditch, you split and stacked the firewood, you did all these things that were really difficult for a kid. Your dad was too busy beating himself up to see how amazing you were, but you did those things. You were a badass. You *are* a badass. You know it, and that's what matters."

It felt as if a giant cog had slipped into place in the gears of my brain, one that had been stuck out of alignment for my entire life. I *did* accomplish some major things. No one else in my class was doing things like that, and while I resented the fact that I was working while they were playing, I still had something to be proud of. I wasn't a failure. I didn't fail at any of those tasks. I accomplished every one of them. Holy shit.

"Disturbance, one to ten."

"Four. Maybe three. It's still fresh."

"Paired with digging the ditch, how true does it feel to say, *I am capable*?"

"Seven."

Nysa set her notepad aside. "Let's put it all in your Pensieve. You made good progress today."

I wondered what my dad would think if he knew how he had impacted me. It was conceivable that his abuse wasn't doled out with the malicious intention of destroying me. If I hadn't been such a sensitive soul, it might not have even phased me most of the time. That thought rang false, though. My dad, the implacable stoic, had been raised just as harshly as he had raised me, and the emotional damage he carried was undeniable. Would he feel vindicated that he had communicated his pain to me, so that someone else would know how he had felt? Or would he feel guilty for unwittingly recreating his own childhood?

He was sixteen years in his grave, and my questions would never be answered. It still felt good to realize that he'd been broken, and that his behavior had been due to his own shortcomings and not mine. It would take some time to come to terms with this new perspective on him, and on myself, but each therapy session brought me a step closer.

I gathered everything and slipped through the foggy surface of my Pensieve. Sorting through the library of books I enjoyed at that age, I picked a western by Larry McMurtry called *Lonesome Dove*. My child-self would love camping under the stars and driving cows across the frontier with his heroes. I left him sitting beside the campfire, staring in awe at Captain Call and Gus McCrae. I knew that he would be okay, and that I would be, too.

Chapter 7

Therapy day was usually a buoy for my mood. The anticipation of solving another one of my lifelong issues was always an exciting prospect. Still, there were times when I couldn't drag myself out of the pit of despair. This was one of those days, and I didn't even try to pretend to be happy as I jogged up the sidewalk and threw open the door to Nysa's office. I was running almost five minutes late, and she was standing in the waiting room when I rushed in, her arms crossed in a faux brusque manner.

"I'm sorry." It came out as more of a growl than I intended. I held back the excuses that stood ready, opting to go with the truth instead as we made our way into her office. "I'm having a bad day, and everything is harder than it should be. And I hate running late. I'm sorry to keep you waiting." I dropped into the chair with a sigh.

"Whoa, slow down." She studied my face. "You're all in a kerfuffle. What's going on?"

Just being in the familiar safe space was calming, and I became acutely aware of all the negative energy I'd brought in with me. I took a deep breath and let it out slowly.

"I'm being butt-hurt about something that happened at work yesterday. I know it triggered an insecurity, but it's really kicking my ass, and I can't seem to let it go."

Nysa grabbed her notebook off the edge of the desk and leaned back on the couch. "Okay, let's talk about it. What happened?"

"I stopped by the vet clinic yesterday afternoon for something. While I was there, Amy, our practice manager, asked me to fill out the banking information on this form so she could finish getting us set up with ScratchPay. I've never even heard of ScratchPay, much less decided to use it, so I was like, what are you talking about? Apparently, she'd talked to Erica about adding it to the ways that people can pay us, and they decided to go with it. I'm the CFO of the practice. I make the decisions on that kind of stuff. And they just cut me out of the conversation. I know it wasn't malicious, but it totally made me feel like a joke."

Nysa jotted down some notes. "Let's elaborate on what you felt. Dig into that."

The rational part of my brain knew exactly how it happened. Amy ran across ScratchPay somewhere, and asked Erica if she knew anything about it. I work from home, so it was totally reasonable that she would ask Erica about it while they were in the office together. Erica owns the practice, so again, totally appropriate. Amy assumed that Erica would talk to me about it and moved forward with getting us signed up. Erica forgot all about it by the time she got home, so I arrived at the clinic the next day outside the loop. But my insecurities didn't see it that way at all, and when they get tripped, their voice is the loudest inside my head. *You don't matter. No one cares what you think. They don't respect you. You are a joke.*

"I've been married to Erica for five years now, so I've been running the vet clinic for a little longer than that. It took me a couple of years to learn everything and take all the business stuff off Erica's plate. Remember that I came into this with almost no knowledge of how to run a business, and medium self-confidence at best. I was six years sober then, but most of my confidence and self-esteem growth has happened since I started this job. The point is that I had imposter syndrome like crazy because I didn't know what I was doing. So, when Erica made a decision like that without consulting me, which has happened a couple of times, it just confirmed for me that I'm not actually running this company, and my opinion doesn't matter. I feel like the boss's husband, with a fake title and busy-work to pacify me. And I know that's not true, but it just crushed me yesterday, and I can't get out from underneath it."

Nysa unrolled the cord and swung the paddles over to me. "I think we should process this while it's fresh. Give me a negative cognition."

"I'm a fraud? I know we've used that one for other things, but it sounds right."

She shook her head. "I don't think that's quite right. Tell me what happened in one short sentence. What's the crux?"

I thought for a moment. "Someone made a financial decision, and it wasn't me." Nysa was staring at me, waiting. "Oh, hell, this is a control thing, isn't it?"

Nysa laughed in delight. "You tell me. Is it?"

The dull anger lifted off my shoulders and was replaced by abashment. "Yeah, it has to be, now that I think about it. How embarrassing."

"Why embarrassing?"

I wear my emotions on my sleeve. I thought about Amy's face the day before when she realized that I was upset. The transition from happy to guarded had been instantaneous as the sparkle left her eyes and her lips tightened.

"I made Amy and Erica feel bad about it," I answered. "My ego took a hit, and I let them know. I should be past that kind of behavior, and I'm embarrassed. Now I have to go apologize to them."

"Let's try to avoid using words like *should*," Nysa said. "You recognized behavior that you want to change, and we're working on changing it. That's where you were yesterday, and next time you'll be better prepared."

"You're right."

"I know." She flashed me a smile with lots of teeth. "What did Erica say when you talked to her about this?"

"She felt horrible," I said. "I told her how it made me feel, probably in a passive-aggressive way, falling on my sword since that's my weapon of choice, and she felt terrible about it. I know her tendencies, too, and I have no doubt that she legit forgot to talk to me about it. She never remembers things like that. It's her weak area. But she also knows how fragile I am sometimes, and she felt bad for making me feel left out. Then I felt like an asshole for being so immature and hypersensitive and making her feel bad for making me feel bad, and it just turned into soup."

Nysa laughed. "How did the discussion end?"

"Pretty good. We apologized to each other, and she promised to be more mindful about deferring to me for that kind of stuff, and I promised to work on not taking it personally when it does happen. It was still hanging on me this morning, as you know, but we didn't go to bed mad, so that was good."

"Okay, let's do some processing. What's your negative cognition?"

"I have to be in control."

"Positive cognition?"

I shrugged. "I don't have to control everything, maybe? I can relinquish control."

"*I can relinquish control*," Nysa repeated slowly, writing it down. "Okay. Paired with Erica and Amy deciding to use ScratchPay without you, how disturbing is it to say, *I have to be in control*?"

Even though I'd already figured out what was going on, the anger still simmered just under the surface. I might've recognized that logically I didn't need to control everything, but my ego clearly disagreed. I had some work to do. "Ten."

"How true does it feel to say, *I can relinquish control*?"

"One."

She switched on the paddles. "Let's just do some open processing and see where your thoughts go."

I felt better already, and the buzzing paddles took me down another level. My shoulders relaxed, and as my muscles loosened, I settled into the chair. The ache of being left out still sat in my stomach, but now I was able to focus on it without the fog of anger obscuring my real emotions.

I drifted back to the previous day when I was standing in Amy's office.

"I need you to sign a couple of checks," Amy said, handing me a stack of paperwork. "That's for the IRA contribution, and the other one is for the landscaping guy. The rest of it is the ScratchPay stuff."

"ScratchPay?"

"Yeah, the new payment method, like Care Credit. I filled out most of it, but it needs some banking information and signatures."

I was overcome with dizziness as a surge of blood rushed to my head. Had Amy decided to just sign up for this on her own? Why? I make the financial decisions for this business. I was her boss, the guy who hired her. What was she thinking by trying to steamroller me with this? I was so upset I couldn't think straight.

I have to be in control. That was the triggering moment. I was angry, yes, but why? I was rejecting the idea of a new payment method. Why? I thought Amy was undermining my authority. Why? What were the facts? I let the scene roll forward another frame.

Amy took a step back. Her pleasant expression shifted to wary.

"Didn't Erica talk to you about this last night?" she asked.

I have to be in control. At this point, I knew that my first assumption was wrong. Of course Amy wasn't doing this on her own— she never had. But instead of letting go of my anger, I expanded it to include Erica. They were teaming up against me. Instead of feeling like the financial manager for the practice, I suddenly felt like a trophy husband, someone who all the staff smiles at, but no one respects or takes seriously. Not that I was a trophy.

Nysa shut the paddles off. "What's coming up?"

"I was just replaying the events from yesterday and trying to identify what I was feeling." I stared at the lampshade in front of me as I gathered my thoughts. "At first I was pissed at Amy because I thought she was taking it upon herself to just do this. But then I found out Erica approved it, and instead of relaxing, I got pissed at her, too. So that's pretty clearly a control thing. I hated the whole concept of ScratchPay simply because I wasn't consulted about it. If I'd found it on my own, I probably would have thought it was the greatest thing ever."

"How about this? You have a thousand things to do every day. You're doing the bookkeeping, paying bills, editing the podcast, writing books, making videos, and all that. ScratchPay is something that didn't need your attention. Amy and Erica handled this without taking time away from your day, even if it was an accident. Do you trust their judgement?"

I took a deep breath and let it out with a sigh. "Yeah, I trust them."

"That wasn't very convincing. Think about it for a minute."

She turned the paddles back on, and I closed my eyes and leaned my head back. Nysa had a good point. If Amy had asked me to check out ScratchPay, I would've spent at least a half hour reading up on it, and we probably would've moved forward with it. The only difference would be that I spent thirty minutes not doing something that I actually needed to do. I preached autonomy and self-management, but when my most trusted team members actually did it, I got offended.

If I came at this with an attitude of gratitude, this exact same situation would be a total win. So why did it hurt my feelings? Did my value come from being the one who made all the decisions? I recoiled in horror at the answer. *Yes.* I knew better than that, but this had been unconscious, and it took someone accidently removing me from that duty to make me see it.

My eyes snapped open as the paddles stopped buzzing. "You're right. I didn't need to be involved in that at all. I just realized I've been drawing value from the idea that I'm controlling everything, like I'm the Wizard of Oz or something. I can't believe I never caught that."

"Now we're getting somewhere," Nysa said. "Where does your value actually come from?"

Instead of letting me answer, she flicked the paddles back on.

It was a good question, and while we'd examined it before from different angles, there wasn't a simple answer. My value comes from a lot of different things, such as living to my capacity. When looking at my role at the veterinary clinic, I certainly did draw value from the contributions I made, and rightfully so.

There were lots of things that I did that others on our staff couldn't do. Hosting and producing our podcast, filming and editing videos, even the bookkeeping. I had a skillset that allowed me to make special contributions. But was the value in the exclusivity? That didn't seem right. Our technicians made contributions every day that were important, but not exclusive in nature. Did the lack of exclusivity impact their value? No, definitely not. The whole notion that no one else could do what I did was bunk. I visualized myself wadding up a piece of paper containing that idea and tossing it in the recycle bin.

My contributions *were* important, though. I just needed to be conscious of why. The things I did made the business function when they were combined with the efforts of everyone else. Whether it was inputting data into QuickBooks, taking the deposit to the bank, or setting up the PA system for a seminar, it needed to be done, and I did it. I was part of the team, and people relied on me. There was value in that.

Outside of the vet clinic, there were other things that made me feel good about myself. The act of getting sober and becoming a person I was proud of was a huge accomplishment. Once that process had started, I was able to let my creative urges bloom. I wrote songs and formed a band. I took art classes and painted landscapes. I wrote books that people enjoyed. I started a side business of building websites that allowed me to create as well as generate income. These things were positive contributions to the world, and they made me feel good about myself.

Over the course of my life, I went from being a self-loathing alcoholic who did nothing to an emotionally healthy business owner. I married a wonderful woman who saw enough potential in me to share everything she'd built. I went from merely existing to thriving. I was growing into my potential. That had value.

The paddles went still in my palms, and I opened my eyes.

"Where does your value come from?" Nysa asked.

"It comes from who I am, and what I do," I said. "It comes from the effort I make, and my contributions. It comes from being actively engaged in growing and becoming a better person. It comes from living to my capacity, and always trying to increase it."

Nysa nodded. "Very good. I like that. And you know you aren't an empty figurehead. All you have to do is look at the annual reports from before you started and compare them to now. Or you can look at your team and compare them to the team that was there when you started. It's not a matter of opinion. You have concrete proof that you've made a tremendous difference to the vet practice. You know that, and Erica knows that."

I smiled sheepishly and looked at my hands. "I know. I just forget that stuff in the heat of the moment. Roland, my mentor when I got sober, used to tell me that first thoughts are for entertainment purposes only. I'm getting better at it, but there are so many things I need to think about between that moment when Amy hands me the paperwork and when I open my mouth. It would be easier if I had a checklist or something. *Do I have any part of this backwards? Am I trying to control things? Am I taking appropriate responsibility? Is there an insecurity being triggered?*" The tension left my shoulders, and I felt better than I had all day, finally able to laugh at myself. "It's hard to be me."

"You're getting there," Nysa said, returning my smile. "Practice makes perfect. Let's check in on your cognitions. Paired with Erica and Amy deciding to use ScratchPay without you, how disturbing is it to say, *I have to be in control*?"

It's funny how much things can change in thirty minutes. All the hurt feelings and negativity were coming from a perceived loss of value. Now that I had defined my real value, the whole ScratchPay thing was a non-event, just another part of the day. "One."

"Good. And how true does it feel to say, *I can relinquish control*?"

A good leader delegates. A good leader trusts the team that

makes the business a success. A good leader doesn't place value on his ability to control people. I was learning to be a good leader, and it was okay to make a few mistakes along the way. "Six."

"That's great! You processed this really quickly. How do you feel?"

The more I learned about myself, the more everything made sense. With the help of my therapist, I was putting more and more puzzle pieces on the board, and the picture was coming together. As I learned how to overcome the emotions that had plagued me my entire life, I felt better about myself. Way better. And each success made me more excited for the next one and filled me with hope for the future. This might have been a quick session, but it felt like a big step forward.

"You know how disconcerting it is when you watch a video, and the audio is out of sync by a second? The lips are moving, but they don't match the sounds. I feel like my whole life has been out of sync like that, and these breakthroughs are putting me back in the groove. Well, not even *back* in the groove since I was never there to start with. I'm finding the groove for the first time ever, and it feels fantastic."

She smiled. "I'm really happy for you. Watching you grow is very satisfying."

"You did that for me."

"Make sure you give yourself some credit," she reminded me. "You've put in an incredible amount of work to get here. Now then, let's quit before we get all gooey with gratitude."

That made me chuckle. I was prone to gushing about my appreciation for her at the end of our sessions. Knowing how to say enough without saying too much was a skill I hadn't refined yet, and I had a knack for making things awkward. "Thank you for saving me from myself."

She laughed. "That's why you pay me the big bucks."

"That's right."

I thought about my role at the veterinary clinic and how my insecurities impacted the people around me. The idea that I could overcome those things with a clarification of my value seemed too easy in some ways. Could it really be that simple? Not that the process of training myself to react appropriately would be easy— I knew better than that. But I was becoming cautiously optimistic that I just might actually grow into the person I've always wanted to be.

Chapter 8

I SAT IN THE WAITING ROOM of Nysa's office building, staring at the hourglass beside the lamp. It was a nice one, with a shiny brass stand and hardware. Whether or not it was an actual antique was anybody's guess. The tiny white grains of sand trickled down to the bottom half, slowly building a mound. Occasionally, the mound would collapse as the vertical pressure became greater than the foundation could handle. The pile would spread out, and the endless trickle of incoming sand would build a new one, which would also collapse. I felt like there was some symbology going on, like it was an artist's rendition of what was happening in my mind as I grew.

The door opened and Nysa stepped out. She was wearing a black dress with tiny specks all over it. As I stood and approached her, I realized they were stars and nebulas, and a huge smile spread across my face.

"You're wearing the galaxy! That's awesome!"

"What, this old thing?" She laughed. "It's one of my favorites. It reminds me how small and insignificant everything is in the grand scheme of things. Makes me feel better when life kicks me around."

I followed her into the office and took my place in the chair. In an odd way, it was comforting to know that even my therapist had bad days. After a few minutes of chitchat, she grabbed the folder from the other end of the couch and pulled out the trauma timeline. While she glanced over it, I took a moment to center myself and do some deep breathing.

"We're up to your mother's suicide attempt. Are you ready to get into that?"

I nodded.

"Okay, give me an overview of what happened."

I pulled in a deep breath through my nose, expanding my lungs, and slowly let it out as she'd taught me to do. "I'm fuzzy on a lot of the details, so bear with me."

"That's fine. Just start at the beginning and we'll work through it."

My mind drifted back to the early nineties. "I was in high school. This was in Wyoming, where we ended up after the whole debacle of the world ending and that author telling my mom she was crazy. I think it was the summer before my junior year of high school. Things were terrible between my dad and me. We fought constantly about everything. All he had to do was walk into a room and I was triggered, angry and ready to argue with whatever he had to say. I probably had the same effect on him. Anyway, my mom had been an emotional train wreck for most of my life, so it was just business as usual as far as I was concerned. My mom getting hysterical wasn't a daily occurrence, but it wasn't out of the ordinary."

"Define hysterical," Nysa said.

I pursed my lips, trying to distil my mother's behavior into a few words. It wasn't easy. "Crying. I was so repulsed that I mostly tried to shut it out, so I don't even have a clear memory other than crying. But she wasn't violent, no throwing things or that kind of stuff. More of an implosion than an explosion, if that makes sense."

Nysa nodded. "Got it. Go ahead."

"I don't know what sent her over the edge, but one day she decided to walk out into the pasture and die. I was in my room, and she was in their room talking to my dad. She was upset, crying, but I tried to block it out and focus on the book I was reading. She went outside, and then my dad comes into my room and tells me to go talk to her. I'm like, *what do you expect me to do?* And he tells me she wants to die, and I'm the only one who can calm her down."

I forced my clenched fists to open and put my palms on my legs. "I didn't want to go talk to her. I'd have preferred to get hit in the face, but even then, for all my defiance to my dad, I couldn't outright refuse him. So, I went out and found her and talked her off the ledge, and she came back to the house."

"Why couldn't your dad talk to her?"

"The only comforting thing he ever knew how to say to her was *I love you.* I think that even he knew that wasn't very helpful."

"Were you upset that she wanted to die?"

I shook my head. "No, but I didn't take it seriously, either. It seemed more like theatrics to me, and I didn't even want to acknowledge it. It was ridiculous."

Nysa made some notes. "How so?"

"The whole thing was absurd. She just hoped she'd die of exposure and misery after an hour. I don't even think she was actively suicidal. If she really wanted to kill herself, there were guns in the house."

"Even if she wasn't serious about it, did it bother you that she was in so much pain?"

"Not really. It sounds cruel, but I felt so emotionally distant from her and my dad that I don't even know if I was capable of feeling compassion for her. All I could think about was how uncomfortable I was. I didn't want to ease her pain. I just wanted to get away from her." Saying it out loud made me feel like an asshole.

"Why did you think she was acting this way?"

"I didn't know, and I didn't want to know. I assumed she wasn't getting an answer from God about something. That was the source of a lot of her distress. She was really trying to reach God, and he wasn't answering." I paused for a moment, thinking. "Now I know that she was so guilt-ridden that she couldn't handle the emotions she was experiencing."

"What did she feel guilty about?"

"Well, I didn't find this out until years later, but she was sleeping with the ranch foreman. In her mind, that was what kept my dad employed there. That's how she justified it to me, anyway. At the time, she couldn't tell me what she'd done, so she talked about a lot of other stuff. Now I know she felt guilty about being unfaithful, especially with how crazy religious she was, and couldn't tell my dad what she'd done, and she just wanted it all to go away. But she was probably carrying some guilt or shame about the whole end of the world thing, too, and dragging us out of Oklahoma in the first place."

Nysa grabbed the paddles and began unwinding the cord as she spoke. "Okay, we've got the situation. You're on a cattle ranch in Wyoming, out in the literal middle of nowhere. Your mom does something she feels guilty about and wants to die, so she wanders out into the wilderness. Your dad has no emotional tools, so he sends teenage Justin out to save her. Does that sound right?"

I grabbed the paddles from her and leaned back in my chair. "Yep, that's pretty much it."

"How old were you?"

"Sixteen."

"Okay. Let's go back to your room, the moment before your dad comes in and tells you to go save her. Try to get in your head at that moment. What were you feeling? And remember that you've got Bob Ross, Dr. Who, and your protection team if you need them."

The paddles buzzed in my hands in the familiar way, left, right, left, right. It was a soothing sensation. I tried to remember that day. Recalling early childhood moments back in Oklahoma was much easier than recalling much of my time in Wyoming during my high school years. That seemed strange, but I left the thought for later and focused on the ranch house.

The ranch was in the scrub flats of the Laramie Valley near Bosler, Wyoming. To the west, the Snowy Mountains framed the horizon. The lower Iron Mountain range was to the east, and much closer. Sage dominated the high desert landscape, with sparse yellow grass providing the forage for the six thousand yearling heifers and steers that spent the summer grazing the eighty thousand acres of pastureland. It was a big ranch, more than you could see in a day of driving around on the bumpy dirt roads that crisscrossed it.

The main house was a modern yellow brick ranch style with a basement. Behind it, the original buildings sprawled out in a semi-organized layout. There was a garage, a bunkhouse, a tiny one-room shack that was probably for the foreman to live in, the original ranch house, and a four-seater outhouse. The old buildings were all gray, with the flaking remains of ancient paint spotting the walls and trim. A big modern workshop had been added, and a long open pole barn to house equipment. To the south of all these buildings, surrounded by a six-foot rail fence, was a huge red barn, also missing more paint than it retained. A fifteen-foot snow fence bordered the west side, which caught much of the blowing snow and formed it into massive drifts in the winter, preventing it from burying the buildings.

My family lived in our big canvas tent for the first summer while we cleaned and fixed up the old ranch house. It was a two-bedroom home, probably from the 1940's, with a big room added on to the back. It had stood empty and derelict for many years before we arrived, save for the dust, bugs, and mice. By my junior year of high school, in an effort to assert my independence and create some separation, I took up residence in the single-room foreman's shack, despite the lack of electricity or heat, but I'd still been living in the main house when my mom went off the deep end.

I lay on the narrow bed in my room, a Steven King novel clutched in one hand. A rough homemade table that I'd pieced together from scraps of two-by-fours and plywood served as my nightstand and held an old lamp and a stack of books. What few possessions I had were either in my dresser or under the bed. In the floor of my closet was a trapdoor that led to the crawlspace beneath the house, which my dad had to access from time to time if the pipes froze. I had long since learned not to have anything in my room or closet that would hinder him, as he had no patience for that sort of nonsense and no concern for the safety of my stuff. If I didn't want it thrown out of the way, then it couldn't be anywhere he might need to go.

"I just don't want to live anymore," my mother sobbed in the next room. The sound of her voice grated on my nerves, and I tried to shut it out and focus on my book. The house was old and the insulation was poor, so I could hear their voices, even if a few words were indistinguishable here and there. The crying became coughing, which was followed by a nose being blown.

"Sweet, I can't fix it if I don't know what's wrong." *Sweet.* The pet name my parents had for each other, which I'd long forgotten. "I love you." My dad's voice was a pathetic whine coming through the thin walls as he tried to console and soothe her. I found it even more aggravating than his angry voice. It seemed unnatural and fraudulent, even though he probably meant what he was saying.

It was impossible to ignore their conversation. If I tried to slip outside, my dad would see me and assign me some heinous task to take out his frustrations, and the thought of cutting firewood and stacking it was even worse than listening to them. It wasn't the work that bothered me, it was the principle of being punished for being present, of being a scapegoat for my dad and his lack of emotional tools.

"What's coming up?" Nysa asked.

"I'm just thinking about the ranch and remembering all the teen angst I had at that point. It's hard to pull the details out. Wyoming is a long way from Florida, especially in my memories. I've thought a lot about my earlier childhood in Oklahoma, but my high school years have stayed pretty buried."

"Do you remember what you were feeling?"

"I had just gotten to that part."

"Okay, get back in there." She flicked the switch to start the paddles, and I closed my eyes.

The dark brown paneling absorbed the light in my room, keeping it dim despite the sunshine pouring in the curtainless window. It was summertime, so I wasn't cold. In the wintertime, I would be under my blanket, holding whatever book I was reading with one hand, putting the other one under the covers to warm up, then trading them out when it was time to turn the page.

My parents' room was on the other side of the wall opposite the foot of my bed. I never went in their room that I can remember. If being in the same house as them made me uncomfortable to a six on a scale of one to ten, the thought of going in there was a solid ten. My sister and brother would go in and sit on the bed and play cards with them, or just hang out, but I never joined them. It would have been like barging into the neighbor's house uninvited: awkward, with the strong potential for conflict.

I focused on being in that moment. The weight of the book sitting on my chest was familiar, so I started with that. I would have been dressed in jeans and a t-shirt, but no shoes or boots. My dad didn't whip me anymore— that stopped when I was about thirteen— but his angry berating was just as painful as the board had been, and shoes on the bed was a known trigger. I lay there on the bed in a room I hadn't thought about in nearly thirty years.

I remembered the musty odor of a house long empty, ripe with mold and mildew. The living room was permeated with smoke from the woodstove, but the rest of the house smelled of damp age, a scent that never went away. My clothes carried both the smoke and the mildew. The dresser had been in the room when we moved in, as had the bed. That musty smell was everywhere, in everything.

The dim yellow bulb from the lamp cast light across the pages of my book, and the smell of decay surrounded me, but I didn't register those things. My mother was having a meltdown on the other side of the wall, and my dad was trying to deal with her. Given the ability, I would have teleported anywhere else on the planet in that moment. Prison, a deserted island, a lifeboat in the middle of the ocean, all seemed better to me than being in that house, listening to them.

Nowadays I know that I'm an empath and that I absorb the emotions of those around me and amplify them in my head. Back then, I had no words for what I was feeling … I only knew that I hated it. My little sister and brother were somewhere else in the house, but they were nearly invisible to me in that moment. My sister, six years younger than me, was almost never the focus of my dad's rage, and my brother was five years younger than her and hardly even on my dad's radar. I never felt a need to protect my siblings. Instead, I resented the freedom they seemed to have from my dad's oppression.

My mom's crying turn into ugly, deep bellows, and the floor creaked as she lumbered down the hall past my closed door.

"Where are you going?" My dad's voice.

"I don't know," she answered, her choked voice so hoarse I barely recognized it. "I don't know. Just leave me alone. I'm going to pray for God to take me. I just want to go away."

I felt no sympathy for her, only disgust. Why couldn't she be a normal person like everyone else? The mothers of my friends seemed so different from her, so *together*. I couldn't imagine them acting the way she was right now. Rolling over to my right, I turned my back to the hall wall as if to shield myself as she passed by. I stared furiously at the book, but the words refused to come into focus, and I was trapped.

The front door slammed a minute later, plunging the house into fragile silence. I knew my dad was still just a few feet away in his room, so my anxiety remained high, but the lack of crying was a welcome change. I heard him sigh deeply, and I hoped he would follow her outside.

I thought about the trapdoor in my closet floor, as I had many times before. If only I'd taken the time to dig a tunnel under there, I could have an escape route. There would be a survival bag down there waiting, filled with food, clothes, and money. I could slip into the closet, drop down through the floor, and be gone from all this. The hard truth of my prison crashed through my fantasy, as it always did. I was thirty miles from town. I had no vehicle, no money, and no contacts. And being in high school, I was too young to get a job and support myself. In reality— hateful, cursed reality— a tunnel would get me nowhere except in trouble when my dad inevitably found it.

The creaking boards in the hall floor alerted me to movement, and a moment later my door opened. I rolled over as my dad walked in, sliding the bookmark into place, and dropping the book. My dad considered reading a waste of time, and even though he'd caught me, I didn't want to make it worse by holding on to the book.

He stood there awkwardly, his lips twitching as he struggled to say something that didn't want to be said. I waited in silence, feeling vulnerable as I lay on the bed, prone and defenseless, while he towered over me. I expected him to tell me we were going to work on something, as that was his M.O. when he needed to get out. Whether it was sawing old fence boards into firewood or working on the truck, he always had something that needed to be done, and just like his dad, he tried to spend every waking moment outside working on something. Along with being his escape from my mother, I think he felt guilty if he wasn't working.

"Do you know what your mother's upset about?" he finally asked.

"No, but since you're in here, I'm guessing I did something." The words came out automatically, bitter and harsh, even though I could tell from his body language that he wasn't there to attack me. It was just so strange for him to be non-aggressive, even apologetic, if not quite verbally, that I didn't know how to handle it. Aggression was all we had by then.

Sadness and confusion flickered across his face, expressions I never saw from my dad. I felt bad for him for a moment, but I immediately choked it down.

"She's sick," he said, finally. "In her mind. I don't how to talk to her." The conversation seemed to be just as painful for him as it was for me, and he looked down at the floor. "She says she wants to die, but she'll listen to you. Go talk to her."

It was the last thing I wanted to do. For all my issues with my mom, I didn't want her to die. I just wanted to get away, to be on my own. Trying to rescue her from an emotional breakdown was the exact opposite of that. He was telling me to go take his place in the conversation, to get closer, to tell her she was going to be okay. If he'd held me at gunpoint and given me an ultimatum in that moment, I'd have seriously considered the bullet. But of course, I was still incapable of saying no to him.

Instead, I sat up and made my way past him and out the door. I was taller than him by then, by nearly six inches, but he still seemed to dwarf me as I stalked by. He stood there motionless as I crossed the kitchen to the mudroom where my boots and the front door waited. On the other side, the space that had represented freedom now seemed to be another layer of hell, waiting to torment me.

"What's coming—" I jumped at the sound of Nysa's voice. "Oh, sorry about that. I didn't mean to startle you."

I pulled myself back to her office with an effort. "I guess I was really in the moment."

She smiled. "Tell me what you felt. What was happening?"

My fingers were gripping the arm of the chair, and I pried them loose. "My mom was crying hard, like somebody had died. My dad was trying to talk to her and find out what she was so upset about. Listening to him trying to be comforting was just awkward as hell. I was lying on my bed, wishing I could just disappear."

"What emotions were you feeling? Were you sad for your mom, or angry, or what?"

I shook my head. "No, I was repelled, disgusted. I wanted nothing to do with her. When she went outside and my dad came in, I thought he was going to work it off cutting firewood or something, which meant that I was going to work it off too, but then he told me to go talk to her. That was worse."

"Why was it worse?"

I grasped for something tangible, some way to turn the feeling into words. "I just… that was his job, not mine. I didn't have any tools to go do suicide counseling on my mom. It was like I was forced into it by circumstance, just because there was no one else to do it."

"I get that," Nysa said. "What did you feel like your position was in the family at that point?"

"I always felt like an outsider. They were a family of four, and I was forced to be there with them, but I was apart from, rather than a part of."

"Why do you think you felt repulsed by her crying, rather than sympathetic?"

The sound of my mom's hoarse sobbing still rang in my ears. "Well, for one thing, she was upset all the time. Maybe not constantly, but after listening to her fall apart for ten years, I just didn't have any supportive feelings for her. It was more like, *Well, here we go again.* This time was just worse than usual."

Nysa wrote something on her pad, then looked back up at me. "What was your gut feeling when your dad told you to go save your mom?"

I blew out a breath and tried to relax, but the sick feeling in my stomach persisted. "I just wanted to run."

"Where to?"

"Anywhere. Anywhere but there, and the farther away, the better. I felt that way all the time in high school, so it wasn't a new feeling, it was just stronger than usual that day."

Nysa made some more notes, then consulted a different sheet of paper. "Okay, let's figure out your negative cognition before we move on. It sounds like you felt like you didn't belong, that you were trapped. You also had a task thrust on you that was inappropriate for a child, and you resented your dad for doing that to you."

"I don't belong in this family," I said. "That was a constant part of my childhood. I didn't feel connected to them. I desperately wanted to be connected to *a* family, to have what I saw other families sharing, but I didn't want it with *them*."

"Okay," Nysa said, writing it down. "And the positive cognition? I belong somewhere? There's a place for me?"

"I like that. *I do belong somewhere.*"

"Got it. Let's check in on that, and then we'll get back into it."

"Ten and one," I said, trying to force a chuckle that I didn't feel.

She jotted down the numbers and turned the paddles back on, and I closed my eyes. A moment later I was standing on the concrete stoop outside the door. We'd painted the trim a dark maroon when we moved in, a gesture to show our appreciation for a place to live besides our big canvas tent, and spilled drops of paint stained the concrete like old blood.

That reminded me of another time, when I'd gotten two puppies from someone in my 4H club. The connection I felt with them was new for me, a feeling of love that I'd never experienced before, and I named them Willie and Pete. I was excited to have something of my own, something that didn't come through my parents, another step towards independence. Something that accepted me unconditionally.

One day while I was at school, after only having them for a few weeks, the puppies found their way out to the corral beside the barn and chewed on the tail of a sick cow. I'll agree that that was bad, but coming home from school to find blood all over the porch and my dogs missing was worse. The fact that the ranch foreman had killed my dogs right on our front porch devastated me. That they hadn't even attempted to wash the blood away insulted me in a very deep way, and confirmed once again that my feelings didn't matter to anyone.

I forced myself to get back on track. Somewhere out in a nearby pasture, my mother was waiting to die. It occurred to me that I could just hide in the barn and pretend that I couldn't find her. But I couldn't go back until she did, as my dad would just send me back looking for her, and I didn't want this to go on forever. There would be no peace, inner or outer, until I talked her down, so avoiding it wasn't going to make it any better, only worse.

I walked down the driveway, past the bunkhouses and the pole barn. Behind them, through the open gate, pastureland stretched for a hundred miles. My mom wasn't going to be far, though. Her psychosomatically frail body, always ailing from one thing or another, couldn't handle walking more than a quarter of a mile on the uneven ground. I pictured her out there, standing on the dirt track amid the sage brush, prairie dogs staring at her in curiosity as she waited for God to strike her with lightning from the clear sky. Or maybe she expected a flaming chariot to take her to Heaven. The whole charade was ridiculous.

I passed the end of the pole barn and reached the gate. Sure enough, my mother was a few hundred yards out in the north pasture, sitting on the ground at the edge of the road. I doubted that she could stand up by herself, not without something to hold on to. Her body was as much of a disaster as her mind.

I felt guilty for being so disgusted by her, but the scene seemed to epitomize my entire life up to that point. Why couldn't they be normal people, just for one day? Why did every single thing they did have to further ostracize me? Other kids from my school were on family vacations at Disney or Yellowstone, posing for funny pictures and laughing together when one of them did something silly. I didn't even know what that kind of family connection felt like, but I could guess that it was a whole lot better than this. Not for the first time, I wished that I'd stayed in Oklahoma when I had the chance.

She looked up as I approached. Her tears had slowed, but her eyes were red and swollen, and a saturated paper towel was clenched in her fist. She sat awkwardly on one hip with her legs stacked on top of each other and jutting out to the side. I didn't say anything. I just dropped down beside her and looked out across the pasture.

Now that I was there, the dread abated somewhat. I was still wildly uncomfortable, but the urge to run away had dulled, leaving a feeling of fatalistic acceptance in its wake. Nothing I could think of seemed right to say, so I waited for her to break the silence.

The wind never stops blowing in Wyoming, and while it often grated on my nerves, it was a welcome companion in this moment. The sound of it rustling the branches of the sage and scrub brush around us covered the sniffing and nose-blowing beside me. Everything about my mother was repellant to me then— her smell, her movements, her fragility, her very presence. I never thought about the times she made me sit in the trash can, or the time she screamed, *Don't you hit me,* as I raised my arm to protect my face from the belt she was swinging at me, which prompted my dad to beat the shit out of me, or the times she would listen to me pour my heart out, then tell my dad about my complaints. I never thought about those things, or a thousand other things that she had done to make me hate her, but I felt them. I felt them, as if each one of them had put a drop of poison into a bottle, and it was overflowing and burning my hands as I carried it around, unable to set it down. The feelings were always there, always raw, and even if I still felt too guilty to admit to myself that I hated her, I knew it was true. And as we sat there in the pasture, both miserable, though for different reasons, I considered how my life would be if she did manage to die.

At sixteen, I had a long way to go before I would escape the brainwashing of my childhood in religion. I wasn't religious, or even spiritual, but the rules had still been steeped in me since birth: Honor thy father and mother, the wages of sin is death, obedience is paramount. Despite my overwhelming desire to be rid of my family, I still felt guilty for thinking ill of them. There had been good times in my life too, and it seemed that that should count for something. I have a hard time remembering any of them specifically, but they were there. And we may have lived on pinto beans for months at a time, but I never starved. I may have gotten sticks for Christmas, but I always had a house, or at least a tent, to live in. It certainly could have been worse. And for all that had happened, she was still my mother, and I loved her in my own way.

She finally broke the silence. "Thank you for coming to find me," she choked out. "You've always been the one I could lean on. My rock. My baby."

And there it was. While she had done horrible things to me half the time, the other half of the time she'd been my protector, my comforter, the one I could talk to about the books I was reading, the one I could share my pain and fear with. She switched seamlessly between roles of friend and foe. At sixteen, I didn't want to be leaned on, not by her, but I was so desperate to be valued by *someone* that I accepted it anyway, even while hating myself for it. "So what's wrong?" I asked.

The sobbing made it difficult to understand her words. "I've just made so many mistakes. I've tried so hard and prayed so much, and I just keeping making horrible mistakes. I can't go on like this anymore. I'm so tired, so tired."

She seemed like an old woman sitting there, but she was only forty-two, younger then than I was as I sat in therapy. I wondered what would be on her list of mistakes, if it would be similar to the list I'd make for her. Deciding that she was a Cherokee medicine woman visionary? Making my dad quit his job and sell the house and all their possessions to go avoid the apocalypse? Coming to Laramie instead of going back to Oklahoma?

Maybe she was thinking farther back than that. Like in the early '70s when she abandoned her college boyfriend to run off to California with some other dude and got pregnant with me, then called her college boyfriend to come rescue her when it all fell apart a few years later. That seemed like a pretty big mistake, one that I constantly reminded both my parents of by my very existence.

None of these thoughts were helping me find an appropriate response. She talked some more, but I don't remember what she said. I couldn't bring myself to reach out and pat her on the back, so I went the verbal equivalent.

"You're doing just fine. Don't be so hard on yourself." The words didn't sound believable to me at all, but she didn't seem to notice the false ring.

"You really think so?"

"Sure. Everybody makes mistakes. Look at Thomas Edison. He had thousands of ideas that didn't work. You just have to keep going and learn from the past, that's all."

She seemed to be mollified by that, and I wanted to shout at my dad and prove to him that reading wasn't a waste of time, that

I'd just used something I read in a book to do his job for him. I knew it was pointless, but the urge was there all the same.

The paddles stopped buzzing in my hands, and I came back to the present with an effort. Nysa's office seemed strange after being in the pasture, very confining. I took a moment to breathe and collect my thoughts.

"What came up?"

I looked down at my hands, trying to find a way to put it all into words. It was hard, as so much of it was abstract thoughts and feelings. "A lot of guilt," I said at last.

Nysa's eyebrows raised. "Guilt about what?"

"About not wanting to help my mom." I met her eyes briefly, then returned my gaze to my lap. "I went out and listened to her and told her a bunch of stuff I didn't really believe to make her feel better, but I hated every second of it. I just wanted to leave, and that's what I felt guilty about. It made me feel like I didn't care if she died or not, and I knew it was wrong to feel that way about your parents."

"Wrong according to who?"

I shrugged. "The Bible, I guess. Even though I wasn't really a believer anymore by then, I still had all that dogma pounded into my head all my life. I didn't overcome that until I was in my thirties."

"Why do you think your dad sent you out to talk to her?"

"Because he didn't know what to say to her."

"Try again. Why do you think your dad sent you out to talk to her?"

"Because he didn't want to deal with it."

"Again."

Nysa clearly felt like I was missing something important. I tried to go deeper, to put myself in my dad's shoes. What was that situation like for him?

Finding empathy for my dad might be a stretch, but if I was on the right track, then seeing my mom self-destruct would probably crush him. After all, he was a product of his own upbringing. His dad had set a high bar on self-reliance, administered the exact same way he had administered the lessons to me: *work harder, try harder, do better, here are all the ways you failed.* The fact that he had to ask me to do something that he couldn't do, to talk to my mom in her deepest moment of darkness, that was him hitting rock bottom, emotionally speaking.

"He sent me out there because, maybe for the first time in his life, he was asking for help. He was acknowledging that I had value, that I was capable of something that he wasn't. He was admitting defeat."

Nysa nodded. "Go on."

"As we've discussed before, I think that maybe he was so buried in his own stuff that a lot of his lashing out had nothing to do with me. I just happened to be there. Probably the same with my mom. She was buried in her world, too. When I think about how self-absorbed I was, how all I could see was my own experience, it makes sense that they were doing the exact same thing. It was never about me being a failure, it was about them feeling like they were failures. It's the same thing as when I was digging the ditch and stacking the firewood. It's all the same thing."

Nysa sat back with a smug grin. "History repeating itself over and over and over."

Now that I recognized that, everything made sense. The bigger picture was starting to take shape for me. I could see how everything was a cycle. Each thing on my timeline was different at the surface, but the underlying things were mostly the same. It was just years of those experiences repeating over and over. Beyond just my timeline, I could see how my grandpa had done all these same things to my dad, and he was just repeating it. This cycle was probably countless generations old, repeating itself over and over for hundreds of years. The only anomaly was me: I was breaking the cycle— both by remaining childless, and by expanding my self-awareness.

"It's really kind of simple, once you get to the core of it," I said.

"Most things are." Nysa scribbled some notes. "So, what happened with your mom?"

"She eventually came back to the house and made supper. Nobody talked about it afterwards."

"Were you happy about that? Disappointed?"

"I guess I was content with things being the way they always were. The devil you know is safer than the one you don't know, right?"

"Hmmm," she grunted. "People always think that, don't they? Justin, your mom was sick. Your dad had no emotional tools to cope with it other than anger. The fact that you didn't feel connected to them was perfectly natural. Would you be able to have a loving, happy relationship with a rabid dog?"

I shook my head.

She continued. "The rabid dog isn't capable of being in a relationship like that. All it can do is suffer, and whoever is around it is probably going to get hurt. It's the same with your family. The fact that you couldn't connect with them isn't a reflection of you, or some inability of yours. They were sick, and the fact that you're so well-adjusted is a marvel. Do you get that?"

"Yeah." I nodded, connecting her statement with what Roland had told me when I was newly sober. *You don't have any obligation to your family just because you're related, Justin. The only one who can obligate you to another person is you.* "Yeah, I really do."

"And do you feel like you belong to a particular family now? Are you a part *of* instead of apart *from*?"

The question made me think about the incredible relationship I have with my wife, and how starkly different it is from the relationship I had with my family growing up. "Very much so. Erica and I are totally in sync. And she introduced me to some people that I really connect with in the way I was always searching for as a kid. I guess I got to pick my family in the end, which is a pretty good deal. We spend Christmas at their house every year, and I can't tell you how much I enjoy it."

"Let's check in. One to ten, paired with your mom wanting to die, how disturbing is it to say, *I don't belong to this family*?"

I pictured my child-self growing up in a house full of broken people. Nysa was right. The fact that I didn't feel connected to them didn't mean there was something wrong with me. The truth was, there was something wrong with them. A lot was wrong with them. "Two."

"And one to seven, paired with your mom wanting to die, how true does it feel to say, *I do belong somewhere*?"

"Seven. Solid seven."

Nysa put her notes down and pretended to dust off her hands. "Well, it looks like my work here is done."

I laughed. "I feel really good. A bit silly, like I should have figured this out a long time ago, but really good. I just have to go through a billion memory cells and reprogram them to frame me as having overcome great obstacles instead of failing to get my dad's approval."

Nysa waved the paddles at me as she wound the cable around the box. "That's exactly what we're doing here. We're rewiring your brain. The more things we process, the more thorough it gets. This is going to change your whole perception of yourself."

When I thought about it, it already had. I didn't see myself as a failure anymore. My feelings on my childhood had already shifted, and now I saw it as an incredible challenge that I had endured, and I had come out the other side stronger and more capable than I ever realized. Never once was I broken. I got up every day ready to fight and defend myself, and when I was able to escape, I shot out into the world and never went back. True, it took me fifteen years to get over it, but I committed myself to changing and improving, and I was succeeding at that.

I was winning.

Chapter 9

Nysa kicked her shoes off and flopped down on the couch as I sank into the chair. She was wearing a purple blouse that matched the purple in her hair, jeans, and rainbow-striped socks. I was in khaki shorts and a plaid button-down shirt, the uniform of the middle-aged white man.

Nysa announced the topic for the session. "Shame of behavior is the next thing on your list. What's that about?"

"That's what I want to know," I joked. "Why the hell am I ashamed of myself all the time?"

"Give me an example."

I thought for a moment. "Back in my drinking days, I would always be ashamed of what I'd done the night before. Things I'd said, or if I was around other people, probably my behavior, too. I think I trained myself to just be ashamed of everything I said and did as a default. I've been sober for twelve years, but I'm still automatically embarrassed when I think about what I said last week in the staff meeting, or whatever. Things I have no reason to feel shame about."

"What was a drunk behavior that you were ashamed of?"

That was an easy one. "Sexual misbehavior. I craved sexual attention, so I did everything I could to get it, even though I was in a long-term relationship. If we went to a bar or a party, I spent a lot of time trying to get laid, sometimes by strangers, sometimes by friends, even right in front of my girlfriend. I recognize now that I was seeking acceptance and approval, no surprise there. Anyway, I always felt horrible about that. Not horrible enough to stop doing it, just enough to hate myself, reject myself, and fuel the need to be accepted by someone else."

"Okay. Give me a current example of inappropriate shame."

I leaned back. "This was in 2015, when Erica and I got married. Her mom was excited to have all the people around, some of whom were friends and family she hadn't seen in years. She thrives in social settings like that. I remember her standing at the top of the stairs, shrieking at a couple that had just arrived. She was trying to be funny by saying something ridiculous, like she does, but it was loud and obnoxious, and I just wanted to crawl under a rock and die."

"You were ashamed of her behavior?"

"Yeah, I think so. I felt like ..." The connections fell into place in my head. "It was exactly like the youth group thing. I felt like people were going to think poorly of me because of her. Come on, how did I not realize that already? I'm taking inappropriate responsibility and creating inappropriate shame. Imagine that."

"Imagine that," Nysa agreed. "And let me guess: the only one at the wedding judging you by her behavior was you."

"Precisely," I said, shaking my head in disgust. "At least I'm consistent."

She laughed lightly. "That does make it easier. Let's go back to child-Justin, before you started drinking. What's the earliest time you can remember feeling ashamed of yourself?"

To me, my entire childhood seemed to be one continuous shame event. I tried to zero in on something specific. There was second grade, when my mom decided that I was not to be exposed to any movies or television shows. The shame came when I had to leave the classroom every time they were going to watch something. One of the teachers would roll in the cart with the television and VCR, and everyone would get excited. Then the inevitable moment, when everything would pause, and all eyes turned to me as Mrs. Middleton directed me to take my book and go to the empty classroom next door. Nothing like experiencing that ostracization on a weekly basis to instill a good base of shame.

That wasn't the earliest thing, though. There were all the Christmases at my grandparents' house, for instance. My parents only allowed me to get socks, underwear, and books for Christmas. No toys, no games. While I could play with my cousins and the toys from my grandparent's communal toybox, I was never allowed to touch a toy gun. That was embarrassing on its own, but nothing like the crushing feeling I got when it was time to open presents. All my cousins would get neat things, like G.I. Joe action figures, or big neon-colored water guns, or cowboy get-ups, and I would have to pretend to be excited about the pack of socks and a book or two. That was always followed by my cousins' questions about why I wasn't allowed to get toys, and I never had any answers.

Reaching back into the bits and pieces of my earliest memories, I happened across one from the house on Oak Street in Bartlesville. We moved from there to Dewey when I was five, so that gave me a waypoint with which to gauge the time frame.

"Okay, I've got something from when I was four or five," I said. "I don't have many memories from then, so this is about as far back as I can go."

"That's fine," Nysa said. "Tell me about it."

I leaned forward in my chair, trying to coax the scene into the light. "I was standing at the kitchen counter, putting silverware away. I sort of remember the silverware drawer being about chin height. I had just grabbed a handful of forks when I heard my dad do his lion roar behind me. That was fine, it was a playful thing. He liked to tickle me, and the roar was a sign that he was about to get me. Like I said, we had good times, too, back then."

Nysa smiled, and I went on.

"But when I turned around, my dad wasn't there. Instead, it was this horrifying monster, and I very nearly peed my pants. I remember seeing my mom off to one side, and she was just standing there, sort of grinning. She didn't seem scared, and that didn't make sense to me, because this, this *thing* was right there in the middle of the kitchen. It was green and had these huge, weird eyes, and a giant black snout. But it wasn't shaped like a living thing— there was nothing natural about it. It wasn't like a bear, or a wolf. It was totally alien, and I had no way to process what I was seeing."

I shifted in my chair. "I didn't know it back then, but my dad was in the Army Reserves. What I was seeing was him wearing his uniform with a gas mask on. It had a hood that came down past his shoulders, so he didn't have a human shape at all. I'd never been scared so badly in my life. It was legitimate. I dropped the forks, and all I could do was scream. There was nowhere to run, and my mom was making no move to rescue me."

"Why were you ashamed of being scared of that?"

"Because even after he took the mask off and showed me that it was him, I had a hard time calming down. He lost patience after a few minutes and called me a sissy. That hurt my feelings. I had the double whammy of the abject terror followed by my dad scorning me. It might have happened before, but that's the first time I can remember being owned by the shame monster."

Nysa made some notes. "Your dad scared you, and then shamed you for being scared."

"Basically."

"What did you feel about yourself in that moment?"

That would have been around 1979, maybe 1980, back when I was an only child. I don't think I had the perception that my life was painful or miserable yet, as I didn't have any peers to compare myself to. Neither of my parents were anywhere near as bad as they would get in later years. I'm sure there were warning signs, but I was too young to recognize them.

It was so hard to remember what my thoughts were like then. I think I was surprised when he turned on me like that. I still trusted them both implicitly, and that moment was a fracture in that trust. For my mom, I felt betrayed that she didn't try to save me from the monster, and for my dad, I felt wrongly attacked. I didn't resent him for scaring me, but rather for making me feel so weak about being scared.

"That might've been the moment when I realized that I wasn't allowed to be a kid anymore," I said at last. "My dad expected me to behave as an adult, and I didn't know how. When he scared me, I should have laughed it off and not dropped the forks. I was learning that it wasn't okay to be honest about how I felt or what I thought. Even if this wasn't the actual first time, it was right around this age that I started putting those pieces together."

"We'll assume it was the first time, just to make it easier. It doesn't matter if it isn't." She pulled the paddles out. "What's your negative cognition?"

This part was always the hardest for me. How do you refine all of the thoughts and feelings into a single, concise sentence? "That I'm ashamed of myself for not being perfect? I'm ashamed of who I am, because I'm a disappointment to my dad."

"*I am ashamed of who I am*," Nysa said, jotting it down. "And your counter?"

"That I'm proud of who I am. I'm good enough."

"*I am enough*." She swung the paddles over to me and adjusted the settings. "Let's get into it."

I stood in the kitchen, forks surrounding me where they'd landed on the floor. My dad was down on one knee in front of me, the gas mask hanging in his hand.

"It's okay, I'm not a monster." He smiled at me reassuringly, but I couldn't believe him. It wasn't possible. He chuckled, but I was too consumed with the massive disconnect in my reality.

"It wasn't you," I said. "That thing wasn't you, and it wasn't that." I pointed to the mask in his hand.

"Then where did it go?" His voice was harder now.

"I don't know!" I cried. "I can't explain it!" The terror of the moment still shrouded me, and as the image of the monster crossed my mind's eye, I involuntarily shuddered and began crying in fear again. "It wasn't you!"

"Fine, be a sissy. And pick up the forks and wash them again, since you couldn't even hold on to them." He turned and stalked out of the room.

I'm ashamed of who I am.

My mother turned away to the sink, abandoning me in my despair. I knew that my dad wanted me to be big and strong, but that's not how I felt. I felt helpless. *I'm ashamed of who I am.* I felt rejected, utterly and completely rejected. My dad had rejected me based on who I was. It stood to reason that if he, my source of all knowledge and direction, rejected me, that I should also reject me. Even my mom had left me hanging. They couldn't have been any clearer.

I struggled to immerse myself in my five-year-old mind. Forty years had gone by since then, so many experiences clouding up my memories. I knew so little at five, and it was impossible to unknow all the things I'd learned since then and just become him. *I'm ashamed of who I am.* The idea that I wasn't allowed to be a child returned. That would definitely become true soon, but was it already beginning then?

I set aside the fear I'd felt from the gas mask and tried to focus on my other emotions. Picking up the scattered forks, I felt like I was being punished unfairly. Or did I? Maybe I also felt like I should've been able to hold on to them, like my dad said. To my young mind, my dad was infallible, a concept he reinforced regularly, so I'm sure I would have agreed with his assessment and even prioritized it over my own. The soil was fertile, and the seeds of self-doubt were being sown.

The buzzing paddles fell silent in my hands.

"What's coming up?" Nysa asked.

I opened my eyes and let them rest on the lamp in front of me. "Well, it's hard to get inside my thoughts back then. They're all fragmented. But I know my parents convinced me even before this that they were always right, no matter what. I couldn't apply it to the monster I'd seen, because the visual evidence was so powerful, but I could apply it to the idea that I was a sissy, and I needed to be more grown up."

"Hmmm." She jotted something down, then looked up at me. "Why do you think he called you a sissy?"

If I put my adult self in his position, I knew I would have done the same thing, which made me queasy. Why had I become so like the man I detested? "I would say that he was frustrated that I wasn't responding the way he wanted me to, and he expressed the frustration with anger. Beneath that, though, he probably felt bad for scaring me so badly, and his response to guilt was also anger. *When in pain, lash out.* It's our family mantra."

"And what conclusions can you draw from that insight regarding yourself?"

It was an easy connection at this point. "That it wasn't about me being a sissy, or even being a kid. It was about my dad's inability to manage his own feelings."

She flicked the switch, turning the paddles on. "Good. Get back in there. Remember your cognitions."

I am ashamed of who I am. Had I spent my whole life feeling a certain way about myself because I misunderstood my dad? Yes, I already knew that to be true. The more pressing problem here was that essentially everything I knew to be true about myself was turning out to be untrue. This was a big thing, and it changed my whole self-identity. But how could I rewrite my entire life with a new perspective on myself and my dad? It would have been so much easier if he were still alive, and we were capable of talking about these things.

I am enough. I knew that to be true, as well. My dad might never have been able to say it, but I could look at my own track record and see it for myself. I had spent my entire life trying to prove something to him, but his failure to acknowledge me didn't mean that my achievements were meaningless. It just meant I had to learn to value myself, instead of waiting for someone else to do it for me. The lesson was a repeat for me. It was the solution to at least half my problems.

I am ashamed of who I am. I was an active alcoholic from the time I was a senior in high school all the way through my twenties. I got sober when I was thirty-two. But with this perspective, I could see how that period of my life was in direct response to everything that had led up to it. Alcohol let me feel good about myself in a way that I'd never experienced. It was also me proving to the world that I was finally an adult, which is what my dad had demanded of me, and no one was going to control me anymore. It was also me, my head loaded with twenty years of emotional pain, self-medicating and lashing out against everything around me. It was a natural reaction to all the trauma I'd experienced. My behavior wasn't good, but it wasn't avoidable, either. I was always going to explode in some way.

Because of the emotional distance between me and my family, I had no concept of how to have a healthy relationship with anyone, platonic or romantic. I didn't know how to show affection, to accept or be accepted, or any of the things that happen in good relationships. I had no role models for healthy behavior, for quality communication, for how to be a man. I knew how to be angry, I knew how to dominate, and I figured out that sex was the ultimate form of acceptance. I moved in with the first woman who was willing to have sex with me twice, and I stayed there for twelve years, continuing to search for acceptance. I didn't know how to *be* accepted, only how to long for it.

I am enough. When my rage and self-loathing had fueled me as long as they could, the lapse in momentum gave me an opportunity to change my life, and I clung to the idea fervently. Change became my new fuel, and with each small success, I tried harder, wanted more. I embraced the pain and freedom of self-discovery, and I became determined to overcome my past, no longer a victim of it. And by all measures, I had achieved that goal. I *was* enough. My wife was all the proof I needed for that. She was the strongest, most determined, amazing, emotionally healthy person I'd ever met, and she thought I was the one for her. Not *a* one, *the* one. If she thought I was enough, then shouldn't I think so, too?

Nysa turned the paddles off. "Where are you?"

I smiled as I opened my eyes. "In a good place. The more

we do this, the more it reinforces my understanding that I had it wrong all along, and that I'm actually okay. I've always been okay; I just didn't know it. If we do this a few hundred more times, I might even be cured."

She grinned as she began winding up the cord on the paddles. "Let's check in quick. You did really good today."

"Thanks. I've been practicing."

I took a moment to put my five-year-old self in my Pensieve. There were a lot of versions of me in there now, all rescued from their perpetual prisons in space-time. I hoped their new vantage point would allow them to see how things were turning out, to know that it did in fact get better. I wanted them to have the freedom to be a kid, to explore the world in their own way, to have some fun. Perhaps I was finally allowing myself to have been a kid and to be clumsy in my attempts at growing up. Maybe I could even allow myself to be human soon. Maybe.

Chapter 10

NYSA GLANCED THROUGH MY FOLDER, then set it aside on the couch and folded her hands in her lap. "I want to talk about your time as an active alcoholic today. I know you've been sober for twelve years, and you've done a lot of work on yourself in that time, and that's really good. I just want to go over things to get your perspective and make sure you're not missing anything important. Sound good?"

I nodded. If there's any aspect of myself that I felt I could speak on at an expert level, it was my alcoholism. After all, I lived it for thirteen years, and I'd been studying it for the twelve years since I quit drinking.

"Okay. Obviously, you were a different person when you started drinking than in the later years, right? So, let's break this up into chunks. Tell me about the beginning, how you discovered alcohol, how it made you feel, and all that."

I floundered a bit at finding a starting point, finally settling on going all the way back to the beginning. "I was thirteen the first time I got drunk, but I didn't have another opportunity to drink for nearly two years. I got drunk that time too, completely hammered. That's not quite true, though, now that I think about it. In ninth grade, before we moved to Wyoming, I managed to go to some parties where I had a few wine coolers, but I didn't really get a buzz from them. That was important, though, because it was the first time I really got to do something social and feel like I fit in, at least a little bit."

Nysa's eyebrows shot up. "Your parents let you go to parties?"

"Oh, no," I said with a laugh. "They had no idea. Remember how I told you about the historical reenactment thing they liked to do?"

She shook her head. "Mountain men and Indians, right? Camping in tipis and stuff?"

"Right. When I got to ninth grade, I was in marching band, and we played all the high school football games. I stopped going to rendezvous so I could play with the band. For all of their faults, my parents did instill responsibility in me, and they didn't have any problem leaving me on my own. And I was really tight with my youth group at church then, so I don't think it ever crossed their minds that I would go to a party with older kids and drink."

"How often did this happen where you stayed home by yourself all weekend?"

I shrugged. "I don't really know, maybe five or six times? We moved to Wyoming that following spring, so however many times they went that fall. They didn't go every weekend, but they went a lot."

"How did you know the high school kids?"

"From choir, and from church. There were two guys who were three years ahead of me that really took me under their wing for some reason. This was huge for me. I was an outcast in my class, but these really cool high school guys thought I was awesome, and that meant the whole world to me."

"Tell me about the parties."

"It was weird for me. I didn't know a lot of the people there, although I recognized some since our junior high and high school shared a campus. I felt like a total outsider, and guilty, like I shouldn't be there. At the same time, I felt totally accepted and protected because my friend was cool, and I was with him."

"Why did you feel like you weren't supposed to be there?"

"Oh, it was everything that was forbidden. The kids were drinking, smoking cigarettes, listening to Motley Crue, and there was a couple in the bedroom having sex. Everyone was talking about it. I was conflicted, because I knew this was all bad stuff, but I was really drawn to it. I didn't know how to do it, but I wanted to participate. I didn't have any booze, of course, but someone was nice enough to share their wine coolers with me. I didn't know what it was, but it made me feel older, cooler. Part of the party."

"Okay, so you got to do that a couple of times, and that helped you begin associating drinking with social acceptance, which you were lacking. Then you moved to Wyoming. What happened there?"

I kicked my shoes off and raised the footrest on the chair, reclining slightly. "I was devastated with the move, because I had just started gaining some independence and finding a place where I belonged. Still, once a nerd, always a nerd, right? Moving to Wyoming was an opportunity for me to reinvent myself. No one knew that I was smart or that my parents were weird, or that I'd been an outcast all my life. I dropped band and choir, and since we lived on a ranch, I got into the agriculture program and became a cowboy. I was still an outcast to a degree, but I made friends with two guys, really tight friends, and we rebelled against everything together."

It was such a tumultuous time in my life. I was brand new to the cowboy culture and trying desperately to fit in with the kids, who had been cowboys all their lives. I was learning that people and things were different in different places. Along with all the other things I was juggling, I was trying to learn how to assert myself, to avoid being pushed around the way I'd been in Oklahoma.

"I don't really remember exactly how it started, but Dusty and I became best friends. Adam came in a bit later, and we became a trio. The connection I had with them was what I'd been yearning for my whole life. When we started drinking on the weekends, it went up ten more levels, to a state of euphoria I didn't even know existed. And my home life was absolute crap, so these two feelings were in serious contrast with one another. We used to drive down by the river, or out in the open range, and just drink beer and talk about how great it would be when we escaped. We all dreamed of getting motorcycles and riding off into the sunset."

Nysa made some notes. "So, in the beginning, drinking made your life better."

"Yeah. I mean, looking at it now, I can see that the connection I had with those two guys was the real emotional driver, but when I was drinking, I could make everything else go away. Booze seemed like the magic elixir then."

"Did you ever get in trouble with it?"

"Yeah, there were a few times. I got a minor in possession charge when I was seventeen. There were a few times when I got pulled over while driving drunk, but I got away with it somehow. Now that I think about it, I had a lot of close calls."

"Tell me about another one."

I thought for a moment. "My senior year, for example, I was in advanced P.E. for my first class of the day. We would spend two or three weeks learning different sports. We went bowling, played tennis, that kind of stuff. We also went skeet shooting out at the country club. This was back when it seemed okay for a teacher to hand a student a loaded shotgun. The teacher was the only adult there, so he was out on the firing line with whoever was shooting. The rest of us were inside the clubhouse because it was frigid cold. Adam and I would go into the kitchen where the fridges were loaded with beer, and just chug as much as we could."

"At nine o'clock in the morning," Nysa noted dryly.

"Right. And then we would go take our turn shooting, hoping the teacher wouldn't smell the beer on our breath."

"That seems pretty reckless."

"It was exciting back then, back when I had no real sense of consequences, or even socially acceptable behavior. If it was against the rules, I was in. I was trying so hard to not be controlled anymore that I looked for ways to show the world that I was wild, and that no one could stop me."

"Did the other kids know what you were doing in the kitchen?"

"Oh, yeah, I wasn't trying to hide it. I wanted to show them how brave I was, how tough and fearless."

"Was that the only time you drank during school?"

I shook my head. "Not hardly. By my junior year, I was staying at Dusty's house most weekends, and we spent that time partying. My parents let me go on the condition that I was at church on Sunday morning. I would take whatever leftover booze we had, and Monday morning I'd sit out in the student parking lot drinking. If there was a lot, I'd come back out at lunch and work on it some more. I even took it inside a few times, but I was so nervous drinking in the crowded halls that it took the thrill out of it. And when people commented on me being drunk in school, I started to worry about someone ratting me out. I still lived in fear of my dad, and while I tried to be as rebellious as possible, I didn't want the school to call him. That was a fight I didn't want to have, because I knew I would lose. If he took my vehicle away, that would be the end of the world."

I often fantasized about how those hypothetical fights with my dad would go. I'd bought my old '76 Chevy Blazer with my own money, and I worked as a dishwasher at a local restaurant to pay for the gas and insurance as well as my alcohol. I pretended that my dad had no power over my vehicle, but if it came to a showdown, he would still take it. I knew he would, and he would say that until I was living out on my own, supporting myself, he was in charge. This conversation had already taken place in reality once, when he threatened to take it and I told him he couldn't, that it was mine. One of the downsides of being cowed by my dad was that I believed he would always win, no matter how hard I fought. I would still fight him on most things, since the consequences were bearable, but I couldn't risk losing my Blazer.

"You were drinking pretty regularly in high school and engaging in high-risk behavior with it. How did you get the alcohol?"

"I bought it myself. There were two places in town that I could reliably buy without being carded for most of my high school years. I lost one of them towards the end. It was a bar, and I'd been buying there for a year, maybe more. I was standing at the register, about to pay for a couple cases of beer and a bottle of some kind, when the secretary from my high school office came wandering over and put her hand on my shoulder. She was all cheery, like, *Hi Justin! Funny seeing you in here!* Then she explained to the bartender how I was one of her students, and that was the end of that."

"Oh, no!" Nysa laughed. "Did she cause you any trouble over it?"

I shook my head. "No, she never told anyone. She gave me a hard time about it when I saw her, though, asking me if I've been to the bar lately, that sort of thing. I only had one liquor store left after that, which made me nervous. By then, having to rely on someone else to buy for me would have been devastating. More for my ego than anything, but it would have caused supply problems too, and drinking was so important to me by then that any risk in my supply was alarming."

"Were you drinking and driving on a regular basis?" she asked.

"Yes. It shames me almost as much as it scares me to death to think about it, but I drove around drunk as a skunk all the time. All through my drinking career, not just back then. How I never killed anyone is beyond me."

Nysa jotted a few more notes and set the folder aside. "Okay, let's move past high school. I assume you left home as quickly as you could when you graduated. When did you start drinking every day?"

"I had my launch planned out, and it was in motion by the middle of my junior year. I joined the National Guard, which sent me to Basic Training the summer between my junior and senior years of high school. The deal with that was that I had to go to drill one weekend a month, and after I graduated, I would go to their school for eight weeks and learn how to be a heavy equipment operator. My plan was to do that to get a head start, and then when I graduated high school, I was going to transfer to the regular army."

"I didn't even know you could join the army at that age."

"Yep. Well, I don't know if you still can, but you could in the early nineties. And I did. That was a big step forward in me asserting my independence from my dad. I didn't end up transferring to the regular army right away, though. After AIT, which lasted two months, my folks decided to move back to Oklahoma. My dad had gotten thrown off a horse and broke his leg in three places, with another two breaks in his arm, and he never really healed up completely after that. Ranch work and the cold winters were getting to be too much for him. At the same time, I was second-guessing my plan of transferring to the regular army, because those eight weeks of training had made me realize that everyone in the army was going to be in charge of me, and that was a scary proposition. I was climbing out of the frying pan, but I didn't want to jump in the fire."

"Seems like a good insight," Nysa said. "What did you do?"

"I moved back to Oklahoma with them. Dusty was going to diesel mechanic school, and Adam was off to basic training, so I had nothing left in Wyoming. Back in Oklahoma, I stayed with my grandparents for a while, then my cousin and I moved into a place together. We drank a lot, but we were broke, and there really wasn't any way for me to change that. It was a tiny town, and there weren't any jobs. That was what finally pushed me over the edge, and I called an army recruiter to see about transferring."

"What was your relationship like with your family during that year?"

"Better," I admitted. "Not living with them helped a lot. I went weeks at a time without seeing them. My cousin and I were learning how to be independent, but neither of us did a great job with that. His mom kept us from starving to death and did a lot of our laundry. That was a huge help, but it also kept me from believing that I was capable of living on my own. That was another alluring thing about going to the army instead of moving to a bigger town and trying to get a better-paying job. The army would feed me, give me clothes and a place to live, and pay me better than anything I was likely to find as a civilian. That lack of confidence followed me everywhere. I wouldn't admit it, but I was afraid that I didn't know enough to take care of myself."

"So you joined the army, because it was the least-risky option you could come up with."

"Yep. And it turned out to be a lot like the move to Wyoming. I went to Ft. Stewart, Georgia, and I made a group of friends that were like Dusty and Adam. I was totally accepted, I felt a part of the group, and we all drank like fish."

"That's when you started drinking every day?"

"Yes. I had money, we all lived in the barracks together, and we sat out front on the picnic table and drank every day when we got off work. I thought I was on top of the world when I was drinking with them."

"But …"

"Yeah. But when I wasn't drinking, and sometimes even when I was, I still felt like I was a fraud, like I was living a lie. I believed, deep inside, that nothing I did was good enough, and that at some point everyone was going to realize that I was actually a big giant piece of shit. No matter how they all accepted me, I didn't accept me. I *couldn't* accept me."

"Why not?"

"Because I was still running from my family. I was still operating— on the inside— as if I was back in high school, or elementary school, miserable and dreaming of escape. I *had* escaped, but I didn't know how to be free, so I just kept on rebelling and being miserable, fighting everyone who had power over me and hating myself for not having the strength to stand up and be feared."

Nysa grabbed her notepad and pen, nodding as she scribbled something down. "There it is. You only knew how to feel one way. Alcohol could help you feel a different way, but you can't be drunk every moment of the day."

"Right," I said. "And the disparity between my sober life and my drunk life was painful. The older I got, the worse it got. I kept drinking more, and it kept working less."

"You've never mentioned a girlfriend, any kind of significant other during this period."

"There weren't any. I wasn't bringing much to the table for

others to be attracted to. I was built like a skeleton, at six feet, two inches tall, and I weighed a hundred and thirty pounds. I had a cheerful personality, but no one wants to date the class clown, especially when he's so over-the-top with his wooing attempts and clearly has no self-esteem."

"When did that change?"

"Being terminally single? While I was in the army. When I was twenty-three, about nine months before I got discharged, I met a woman in a bar. My buddies and I were going out six days a week then, partying every night. I hit on women all the time, and I finally found one that was willing to take me home."

"And she was a big drinker, too?"

"I think she became more of a drinker with me around, but yeah, she liked to party."

Nysa scribbled a few more notes. "Okay, I think that's a good place to stop for today. Meeting this woman and moving in with her was a big turning point in your life, so I want to give that plenty of time."

I wasn't going to argue with her. We'd covered a lot of ground, and while it had included the best times of my life at that point, the memories were a double-edged sword. Thinking about my life back then in this kind of detail was emotionally exhausting. Now that Nysa had suggested quitting for the day, I realized how fried I really was.

"I think you have a pretty good perspective on why you started drinking, and what you were searching for," Nysa said. "If we look at all the things you experienced up to that point, we can see that you had an incredibly negative concept of who you were. Your understanding of the world was that you were going to fail and that no matter how hard you worked on something, you'd be punished. You felt invisible, used, and unwanted. Your mom was circling the drain, you couldn't even have a conversation with your dad without fighting, and the only thing you could think of was getting away. Alcohol seemed like a miracle solution to you. It made you feel good about yourself, something you'd never experienced. You had fun. You were out of your parents' control. But it wasn't a real solution, and it only took a few years for the facade to start falling apart. Does that sound right?"

"That sums it up pretty well," I said. "And it makes it really obvious that everything in my life was leading up to that. I was destined to be an alcoholic long before I ever had my first drink. It's a miracle that I didn't get into drugs, too. I was a perfect candidate for it."

She nodded. "For sure. Let's leave it at that for now. We'll get into the rest of it next week."

I drove home slowly, lost in freshly unearthed memories. So much of my past was shrouded in guilt and shame, but it was becoming clear that I was doing that to myself, and it wasn't necessary. The events happened, yes, and I'd acted inappropriately many times, but those things didn't define me. They were merely waypoints in my past, markers to show how far I'd come. My self-awareness and commitment to change were the important things. The only shameful thing would be if I recognized the behaviors I didn't like but did nothing to improve myself.

Instead of beating myself up for where I came from, I decided to start celebrating how far I'd come, and looking forward to where I was trying to go. Being positive in my self-speak was something I could start working on immediately. Most people told me they couldn't even imagine me drunk. That was a wonderful feeling. They weren't concerned about who I was twenty years ago, and I shouldn't be, either. It was time to start living in the present.

Chapter 11

THE DARK, COOL WAITING ROOM was a relief from the oppressive heat and humidity outside. I didn't even have time to sit down before Nysa appeared at the other door. She beckoned me to follow her, and we made our way to her office.

"How are you?" she asked as we got settled in.

"Pretty good. Strange, but good. I've been in a weird head space this week."

"Strange?" She laughed. "I don't think anyone has ever said that to me before. *I'm strange, how are you?*"

I couldn't help but laugh with her. As a writer and an avid reader, I loved quirks of language, sometimes even my own. "I'm honored to be the first to use it in a sentence."

"What's been going on? What have you been thinking about?"

"Memories. All this dredging up the past has me remembering things I haven't thought about in a long time. I got on Google Maps and looked around Laramie on the street view. So much has changed that it was disorienting. It's barely even the same town. That gave me a sense of loss, in a way. It's like the coordinates are the same, but the people are gone, the businesses are gone, there are whole new sections of town that weren't there before, and all of that. The Laramie I knew only exists in my mind. It's scary, in a way."

"Have you been back there since you left?"

I nodded. "Once. I left there in 1994, and I didn't go back until 2010. It was different then, too. I didn't recognize anything. I didn't stay long, maybe an hour, just enough to eat lunch and poke around for a minute. That was during my motorcycle trip from Georgia to California, so I was just passing through, anyway."

"I guess it's true that you can't ever go back, huh?"

"It is," I agreed. "The longer you're gone, the less there is to go back to. And no matter what, it can never be like it was."

"What were you hoping to find?"

I wasn't prepared for that question, and I had to think about it for a minute. Prior to 2010, I had often thought about Laramie, though only certain aspects of it. I had a strong nostalgia for my friendship with Dusty and Adam, and I hadn't spoken to either of them much since high school. When I began planning my trip in 2010, the thought of going to Laramie was exciting, even though I knew Dusty and Adam were long gone.

"I think I was hoping to be in a familiar place, which would give me a sense of connection to the good times I had with my friends. My fantasies leading up to my arrival there were mostly me going to some of the places we used to hang out and reminiscing. I probably even thought I'd find someone standing nearby who wanted me to tell them stories about the good old days, or something ridiculous like that."

Nysa smiled. "And what really happened?"

I let out a sigh, remembering the confusion I'd felt as I pulled into town. "It was a disaster. Right off the bat. The Walmart was on the wrong side of the road when I got off the interstate, so that got me disoriented. There were a bunch of subdivisions in what used to be open desert. I tried to go to the pool hall where Dusty and I had spent so much time, and I couldn't even find it. I think the whole building was gone, but I wasn't even sure which block it'd been on. Then I tried to go to the western store where I'd bought all my cowboy boots and brush popper shirts. It was gone, too. That was a place I liked, because it smelled like leather, and when I bought those flashy, expensive shirts, I felt like I was somebody. But, yeah, the only things I found that hadn't changed were the high school and the National Guard armory where I first joined the military. I was really disappointed."

"What did you do?"

"I went to Hardees and ate a hamburger and got back on the road. Finally, sixteen years later, I got to roar out of Laramie on a Harley and ride off into the sunset, but it wasn't satisfying at all. It did kind of squelch my nostalgic dreams of going back, though. I don't have any desire to go back now." I paused for a moment. "Maybe I wouldn't mind going back to the ranch, I guess, just to bury some skeletons."

Before I arrived in Laramie, my plan had been to spend a day there, poking around, go to the ranch, and all that. Once my initial trip through town proved to be a bust, I talked myself out of it. I was afraid of taking the motorcycle down the miles of gravel road to get to the ranch, for one thing. There was one particular curve that I was worried about, as it was steeply banked. The road used to get washed out around the cattle guards, too. It would have been an hour or more of my afternoon to ride out there and back, and since I had decided to push on to Rock Springs, I didn't want to waste the daylight. Secretly, I was also afraid that seeing the ranch might be just as disappointing as Laramie had been. A lot of good moments happened there, but a lot of bad ones had, too.

Nysa pulled out the notebook and glanced over her notes. "Are you ready to get to work?"

"Yep."

"Okay, we left off last week at the end of your time in the army. You were drinking daily with your friends, and while you were having a lot of good times, you were still fighting against everyone that you perceived as a power figure, and you felt bad about yourself. The only place you had any status or equal footing was with your drinking buddies. And then you met a girl."

"And then I met a girl." It was a major mental gear shift to get from revisiting Laramie to when I met Kari, and I spent a minute composing my thoughts.

I was twenty-three when I met her. I wasn't a virgin, but I wasn't far from it, and she was the first real girlfriend I ever had. She was also nine years older than me. At the time, I was only conscious of the romantic and sexual connection, but in retrospect, I can also see where elements of stability and nurturing were also in play. She was the mysterious older woman, experienced at life and secure in her place in the world, at least compared to me.

"I remember the night I met her. I was actually interested in her friend, but my invitation to dance got rejected, so I asked her. She said yes. I was a terrible dancer with no coordination, but as long as she was willing to pay attention to me, I was willing to keep trying. I totally abandoned my friends and focused on her. And beer, my liquid courage. I was focused on that, too."

"And you took her home?" Nysa asked.

"Yeah, when the bar closed. She started to leave with her friend, who was there with her husband, as it turned out, but she changed her mind and asked me to take her home. It was a last-second drunk decision that changed the course of my life. And hers, too."

"Instant relationship?"

"Instant. It was a weeknight, so I had to go to work the next day, but when I got back to my barracks room that afternoon, she'd left a message on my answering machine inviting me to come back over. I didn't spend another night in the barracks for months. I slowly moved my clothes to her apartment, a few more each day. It was a state of euphoria for me, at least for the first two weeks."

Nysa's eyebrows shot up. "What happened at the two-week mark?"

"Her son came home from visiting his dad."

"Oh, she had a child," Nysa said. "Yeah, I can see how that would change things for you. How old was he?"

"Ten."

"And what did he think about coming home from his dad's and finding you there with his mom?"

"He didn't think too much of it at all. He was mentally handicapped, so he didn't have all the same communication tools as a regular kid, but he made it clear that I didn't belong there."

"And how did you handle his rejection?"

My face flushed with shame as I thought about it. While I was far more patient with him than I'd ever been with anyone else, I still took it personally when he acted out against me. "Poorly, at least sometimes. I was still an open wound at that point."

It took me a few months to learn how to talk to him and how to understand him. While he had his moments of rage against me, where he would scream at me to get out, we also got along really well a lot of the time. I learned early on that he took his cues on how to feel about something from those around him. If we were excited, he was excited. If we were angry, he was angry. That was a tough situation, but I was a quick study, and I had strong motivation to make it work. If you'd asked me then, I would've told you it was the sex, but now I know it was acceptance, security, and a family that I wanted to be around.

"How did her son impact your drinking?"

"Hmmm, that's a good question. It didn't slow me down at all, but things definitely changed. On weeknights we would drink at home. He hardly ever saw me when I wasn't drinking. Early on I taught him how to get me a beer and take the lid off. He loved having a sense of purpose, and I used that to make him my bartender. We made it a game, and while it was probably wrong in some ways, it was what we used to build a relationship. But in terms of impacting my drinking, I think he made me be self-aware to a degree. I was very conscious of how I managed his emotions because it was a whole lot easier to keep him happy than it was to deal with him in a rage. I was a part of his life for twelve years, and that was a constant."

"And did he ever accept you fully?"

"Oh, yeah, for sure. We became really close. By the second year, and from there on out, my relationship with him was far stronger than my relationship with his mom. He kept us together far longer than we ever would have been without him."

Nysa shifted her legs to the other side. "You've talked before about shame with your drinking. How did that factor into this part of your life?"

Shame. It was a wet blanket that shrouded my memories of an entire decade, tainting them with mildew and the smell of decay. "It was the same problem that I'd had in the army. From an emotional standpoint, all I knew how to do was seek acceptance. I was programmed to search, search, search, and I didn't know how to act when I found what I was looking for. All I knew how to do was keep searching and keep feeling discontent. And that's what I did."

"How did that manifest?"

"I switched jobs a lot. I had a bad attitude about everything; I could give you a list of ten problems with any situation, but I'd be hard pressed to find more than two good things. But that's not what I was ashamed of. That part was about infidelity. Every time we went out to a bar or to a party, I got drunk and tried to find a girlfriend, even though I already had one. It was unconscious, but sex was the ultimate form of acceptance in my mind. So I kept looking for it. Fortunately, I didn't find it much, and most people were used to me being *that guy* and hitting on everyone, but still, every morning after a night out, I felt absolutely horrible about myself. Wretched."

"How did you deal with that?"

I shrugged. "I started drinking again as soon as possible. By the time I was three or four beers in, I'd feel better about things, and then I'd start the cycle all over again. And we'd both get drunk at home on weeknights and fight about things, usually her relationship with a gay couple that I knew she liked way more than me. I felt rejected, even though I was driving her away with my behavior. I was a self-fulfilling prophecy of rejection and unworthiness."

Nysa wrote for a minute. I stared at the ceramic snail on the end table, fighting off the familiar shame that was returning with the memories. My behavior had baffled me then— I didn't understand why I couldn't stop acting that way. I truly believed in my core self that I was broken, that I belonged in a padded room somewhere. The thing that kept me from checking myself in to a mental hospital was the fact that I wouldn't be able to drink, and drinking was the only good thing I had. I couldn't bear to give it up. How could I ever be happy without it?

"You got to a breaking point with your drinking," Nysa said, bringing me back to the present. "Was there a crisis event? What happened to make you stop?"

"There wasn't an event, no dramatic moment. I just got more and more miserable. The idea of dying seemed more and more appealing. I hated my girlfriend, I hated my job, and I hated myself. In an effort to control my sexual misbehavior, I had stopped drinking around other people, so I was isolating and drinking alone every night. She was still going out, and I stayed home with her son and got drunk and watched movies or played computer games.

"I had a buddy at work that I used to hang out with during the day, especially in the mornings. He had a drinking problem too, and we would complain about our hangovers, and sort of help each other feel better about what we were doing to ourselves. We talked a lot about taking a few days off the booze to give our bodies a break, but neither one of us ever made it more than a day. I don't remember the exact conversation, but I made a joke once about having a drinking problem. It wasn't bad enough to go to a meeting, but something had to give. I was joking but still being truthful. He replied that he was actually thinking about going to a meeting, and that changed everything for me. If he was cool enough to go to AA, then I was, too."

"And did you?" Nysa asked.

I nodded. "I did. That conversation happened on a Monday. I went home that night and drank three beers while I read through the Alcoholics Anonymous website. There was a meeting at a church two blocks from my house that Thursday, which I felt was rather serendipitous. Those were my last three beers. I haven't had a drop since."

"How about your friend?" Nysa asked. "Did he get sober, too?"

"For a while," I said. "He made it ninety days before he decided he wasn't actually an alcoholic and went back to drinking. But that was okay. It got me where I needed to be."

"Did being sober change how you felt about things? About yourself?"

"No, not at all. Well, it did at first, but that was just the euphoria of drying out, and it didn't last long. But what it did do was hit the pause button for me. It helped me break that cycle of destructive behavior. And then I started gathering some much-needed information. I learned that alcohol wasn't the problem, it was a symptom. Quitting drinking didn't solve my problems, but it let me figure out what they were so I could start working on them. It was the beginning of my journey into self-awareness."

"And your girlfriend?"

I shook my head. "When I quit drinking, she doubled down on hers. My relationship with her son got better, but things with her were past the point of fixing by then. I realized that alcohol was our common denominator, and when I took that out of the equation, we didn't have any way to meet in the middle. We limped it along for about a year and a half after I got sober before we finally gave up on it."

"What was it like trying to get sober and living with someone who was defiantly drinking around you?"

I thought about all the times I came home from work to find her and her friends at the house, drinking and having a good time. Just seeing the cars in the driveway was enough to send me off the deep end. I was sober, and I was starting to learn about myself, but I still hadn't developed many emotional tools. I knew how to be angry, and how to hurt people with my words. My effort to curb my destructive behavior in those days was usually avoidance. I would either drive right on past the house and go somewhere else, or I would go in, be polite to everyone, and disappear into the bedroom and hide until it was over.

Oftentimes that involved hanging out with her son and playing a video game, so it wasn't all bad. But I would be mad at her on the inside, and it would smolder until I couldn't contain it anymore, and then I would say something hurtful to her. Later, I would be ashamed of myself for it. No alcohol, but the same cycle of perceived rejection, followed by anger, followed by bad behavior, followed by self-loathing.

"It was rough," I admitted. "Sometimes I was holier-than-thou. Sometimes I just shut it out. But when she would go out on Friday night and not come home until Saturday afternoon or Sunday, I would really be miserable. I was torn on those occasions, because I was glad to not have her around, but it still triggered my feelings of being rejected, and I didn't know how to handle that. Maybe if I'd started going to therapy right away when I quit drinking, I could've navigated that time better, but I didn't."

Nysa smiled. "You don't know what you don't know, right?"

I laughed. "Fact. I listened to a podcast on leadership development a while back, and it really struck me. They said there are four states of being. Unconscious incompetence, where you are bad at something, and you don't know it. Conscious incompetence, where you're bad at something, but you do know it. And on the other side of the coin are unconscious competence, where you're good at something but you aren't aware of it, or not aware of why you're good, and then conscious competence. That's where you've trained and studied, practiced, and you know what you're doing."

"That's pretty useful," Nysa said.

"Oh, for sure," I replied. "In my drinking days, I was in unconscious incompetence regarding being in a relationship and managing my emotions. In early recovery, that began to transition to conscious incompetence. I was still bad at those things, but I was becoming aware of it. Since then, it's been a journey towards conscious competence. Learning how to be intentional instead of reactionary. If you prefer the mob movie reference, I spent most of my life as the guy tied up in the trunk, and now I'm learning how to drive the car."

Nysa's eyes danced with amusement. "And who are the other people in the car? Who's in the trunk now?"

"All the people in the car are me. Various versions of me. Helpless Victim Justin in the trunk. Angry Violent Justin in the passenger seat, looking for a fight. Cautious Fearful Justin in the back seat, becoming aware, but with no confidence to take action. And Confident Self-Aware Justin is driving." I paused for a moment as the analogy developed further in my mind. "I guess my position in the car depends on my headspace at any given point. I have the tools now, so I can choose which Justin I am. I just don't always remember that I can change from one to another in the heat of the moment. Does this sound ridiculous?"

"No! This is really good. When you were in unconscious incompetence in early sobriety, you were going back and forth from the trunk of the car to the passenger seat, right? Either being a victim or attacking."

I nodded. "I think that's actually where I spent the first thirty-fours years of my life."

I thought back to my sessions with Roland, my mentor in recovery. We had most of our discussions in his meditation room. The walls were lined with shelves, overflowing with ancient books and magazines, which gave the room a faint musty smell. We sat on pillows on the floor, as the single chair in the room was buried under a stack of books.

Roland was an imposing figure. He wasn't big or strong, none of the physically intimidating things, but he carried an aura of authority that was beyond question. He was old, in his late seventies when I met him. Half Apache and half Mexican, his skin was always dark, and his straight black hair fell past his shoulders. His glass eye pointed slightly to one side, which was disconcerting, but his deep voice was strong and full of life.

"No negative self-speak," he told me, over and over. "It's the first commandment of healing. That means you don't get to call yourself bad names or think bad thoughts about yourself. No beating yourself up for past behavior. I mean it. If anyone beats you up, it'll be me. I'm an old, gay, one-eyed Apache Vietnam veteran, and I was a martial arts instructor for thirty years, so I can do it. Do you understand?"

"I understand," I would say. "And I'm trying, I really am." But training myself to be nice to myself was difficult. Stunningly difficult.

"Second commandment," he would say. "If you catch yourself breaking the first commandment, refer to the first commandment."

He would make me tell the story of an event that I felt shame about over and over until I could lay out the facts without saying something disparaging about myself. It was an exercise to create awareness, and it opened my eyes to just how negatively I thought of myself in an unconscious way. Unconscious incompetence.

"You train others how to treat you," he would say. "If you treat yourself like shit, you give others permission to treat you like shit. How are you going to expect people to treat you well when you spend all your time explaining to them what a piece of shit you are? You say, *Hey world, I'm a piece of shit. Here I am, a nothing with no value. Why don't you love and respect me?* No negative self-speak. That teaches you to think positively about yourself, but it also teaches others to treat you better."

I spent three years with Roland, learning how to stop hating myself. It was painful, it was difficult, and it was slow. But it worked.

Nysa brought me back to the present. "When you examine your past from a perspective of conscious competence, where you can see that Past Justin was operating in a state of unconscious incompetence, how do you feel about yourself, then and now?"

I let out a long breath. "I can see that I was on a trajectory, like a comet hurtling through space. I was the way I was as a direct result of my environment, and I couldn't have done anything different than I did because I didn't have the information at the time. The most natural thing in the world for me to do would be to continue on that trajectory, repeating the cycle of destruction that all the generations before me had repeated. Fortunately for me, I got close enough to something with enough gravity to change my trajectory. I was acted on by an outside force, and that gave me what I needed to change everything."

Nysa nodded a few times as she scribbled down some notes, and I continued.

"I can't be mad at myself for who I used to be. It's not logical to expect myself to have come into adulthood with some magic bag of life tools, emotional health, and self-confidence when I came out of an environment of complete dysfunction. Of course I was a raging alcoholic. Of course I was a sexual predator. Of course I was a horrible spouse to Kari, and bad employee and friend. I didn't know how to be anything else. But I managed to overcome all that. I defied the odds. I'm becoming someone I'm proud of. And I feel really good about that."

"So, what emotion do you feel when you think about thirty-year-old Justin?" Nysa asked.

I thought for a moment. That was two years before I quit drinking, so I was in the darkest part of my life then. "Compassion. Sadness. There was so much I didn't know."

"And what emotions do you feel about yourself now?"

"Proud of all the things I've accomplished and who I'm becoming. Excited, because I'm exploding into so much more than I ever was, but I'm starting to realize this is just the beginning, and I have a ton of potential to grow. I still get down on myself for not behaving the way I want to all the time, but I'm more aware of the complexity of the human condition, and I'm trying to accept that I can make mistakes and still be on a good trajectory. I can be a good person who does bad things sometimes, that losing my temper once in a while doesn't make me a bad person. So I guess I feel compassion for current me too, but in a different way. I'm slowly allowing myself to be human, if that makes sense."

"It does," Nysa said. "We've talked before about how you don't expect other people to be flawless, and you are forgiving of their mistakes, and how you're trying to apply that to yourself, as well. I'm glad you can see your past from that perspective. I think the analogies help you grasp the picture as a whole, and I like the comet idea. You were flying along that path because when you escaped the gravity of your parents, that's the direction you were going. You had no way to steer, and no other elements than those from your parents' star system, and it was lacking a lot of important things. But you made your way to another star, and now you're gathering the things you need to become self-propelled. You're evolving."

"Exactly!" I laughed. "That's perfect!"

And it *was* perfect. I was evolving, growing from a simple organism that had no perception of itself or its impact on the world around it into a complex being. And the more I evolved, the faster and more complex I became. Learning that most of my wiring was faulty allowed me to rewire myself in a way that stripped away the hurdles that were slowing me down. That was the therapy, helping me see myself through the lens of knowledge and understanding. I was reinventing myself, deleting all the bad coding and replacing it with things that would make life a good experience, something to savor rather than endure.

I called Erica on my way home, just to hear her voice.

"Hey."

"Hi. I just got out of therapy and wanted to see how your day is going, if you've got a minute."

"Yep, I'm at the clinic waiting for my next appointment to get here. They had a hard time getting the horse on the trailer."

There were so many things I wanted to tell her. She had no way of comprehending how much better my life was with her as my partner, and I had no way to express it. All I could do was keep making meager attempts.

"If love was measured with horses who wouldn't get on the trailer ... never mind, that one doesn't work. If love was measured in miles, then a trip to Jupiter would barely express what I feel for you in a minute. Just so you know."

"Hmmm. If love was measured in cubic centimeters, the *U.S.S. Enterprise* wouldn't be big enough to haul mine to Jupiter with us."

I smiled, even though she couldn't see me. "Sorry it took me so many years to find you."

"It's okay," she said. "We were both getting ready, that's all. How was therapy?"

"Really good. If you come home at a decent hour, I'll tell you all about it."

I drove the rest of the way home with a grin on my face. If the first thirty-eight years of my life were the price I had to pay to have the life I had now, and to be who I was becoming, then it was totally worth it.

Chapter 12

NYSA WAS WAITING IN THE INNER DOORWAY as I entered the office building.

"How's the writing going?" she asked, leading me inside.

"Really good. It's like a three-hour therapy session every day." I gave Cerby a quick scratch behind the ears as we settled in.

"That's awesome! I'm excited that you're putting so much time into this project. It's going to be like a rocket booster for your healing process."

I smiled. "It already is. Writing is amazingly therapeutic."

"Definitely." She opened my file. "Let's get busy. It looks like we're working on authority figures today. What's that about?"

It had been nearly a year since I'd written the list that she was looking at, but I immediately remembered what I'd been thinking. "Ah, yes, authority figures. Cops, judges, supervisors, pretty much anyone who has power over me. I get two responses to them. First is fear, or maybe anxiety. My hands shake, and I feel totally helpless. The other response is rage. I get belligerent, defiant, like I'm trying to prove to them that they don't have any power over me. I know it's all tied to my dad, but I'm not sure how to overcome it."

Nysa nodded. "I totally get that. I've had the same response, anxiety and hostility. It sucks."

"Exactly," I said. "And it isn't even justifiable most of the time.

For example, I had to go to small claims court to try to collect payment from a former client, and I felt it there. I was the plaintiff, not the defendant, but I was still shaking like a leaf, and I had to restrain myself from being an asshole to the judge. It was absolutely ridiculous."

"What's another example?"

I thought a moment. "I got pulled over on my motorcycle a few years ago for speeding. Like, fifty-five in a forty-five mile-per-hour zone, nothing crazy. The cop was super cool, and wasn't trying to intimidate me or anything. Still, my hand was shaking so bad when I handed him my license that he took a minute to try and calm me down. He told me I didn't need to be nervous, that everything was okay."

"That was decent of him," Nysa said.

"It was. I was embarrassed for appearing so weak, so I lied and told him I was shivering because it was cool out. I wasn't even consciously afraid of him, but my heart was pounding, and my hands were shaking, so it probably looked like I was ready to burst into tears."

"What would you have rather felt?"

"That we were on equal footing, I guess. Not nerves."

Nysa looked at her notes. "You said it happens with supervisors, too?"

"Yeah. Less nervousness, more defiance, but still both."

"Okay, let's take it apart. What makes you feel nervous and defiant around these people?"

On the surface, the easy answer was that I was still trying to get out from under my dad's thumb, even though he'd been dead for twelve years. Anyone who had control over me made me feel like I was powerless, a victim.

"I think it's more emotional extremism," I said. "When someone has *some* power over me, I take it all the way, and in my head, they have *all* the power, and I don't have any."

"And if they have the power to control you ..." Nysa prompted me.

"Then I have no value," I finished. "Which is patently absurd."

Nysa tilted her head for a moment in thought, her purple hair flashing in the lamp light. "Let's talk about how you want to feel in that moment. What makes you feel powerful?"

I didn't have an answer ready for that one. "Well, let's see. I want to be able to act according to my morals and not feel forced to step outside of that. The same with dignity, I think, not sacrificing that. And I want to feel respected for my intellect and ability to make decisions."

"Hold on a minute," Nysa said, pulling her phone out. "Let's look at the actual definition of some words, because I think what you're describing as power is actually more like strength. Let's see what the definition of power is."

She was right.

"Here we go. There are a lot of definitions for power, but I think this is the one we're looking for: *The ability to influence others, command over people*. Let's look at strength." She tapped the screen for a moment. "*The ability to withstand pressure*. That's pretty good. It also lists courage."

The light bulb came on inside my head. Had I been misunderstanding the dynamic of these relationships all my life? It seemed so. Nysa tossed the paddles to me, and I closed my eyes, ready to dig deeper.

"Let's just do some open processing to start with. Think about how these definitions impact your perspective on things."

I nodded without opening my eyes, and the paddles began to vibrate in my hands, left, right, left, right. The definition of power as being the ability to influence someone else made total sense. It had nothing to do with any of the things I had listed as being important. The cop writing me a ticket wasn't doing anything that took away from my value as a person. He was simply writing me a ticket for speeding. He had the power to take some money from me, but only because I broke the rules and gave him that power.

Strength, on the other hand, I had lots of strength. I searched for a visualization to help me get some perspective. I pictured a ball of energy surrounding me, a forcefield made up of my strength of character, that would protect me from anything. My morals and values, my intelligence, my commitment to my belief systems, all of that was in there, and it finally clicked— I don't value power, I value strength.

The paddles stopped buzzing and I opened my eyes.

"What's coming up?" Nysa asked.

"A lot," I said. "As is often the case, I've been confused about this my entire life. Lack of power has always been my perceived dilemma, but power wouldn't have changed anything for me. It's meaningless, just a function of position. Power doesn't have any value, and lacking it doesn't diminish anyone's value. It's just a mechanism to make society function."

"Okay," she said, switching the paddles back on. "Get back in there."

My bosses over the years were all in a position of power over me, and my insecurities made me a hard employee to deal with. But how much power did they really have over me? Enough to direct my activities while I was being paid. In the scope of my entire life, and the autonomy I have as a human being, a supervisor might have ten percent power over me, tops. Probably more like five percent. And yet, even though they were only asking for five percent control over me, I was giving them ninety-five percent, and then resenting them for it. It was an embarrassing realization.

My dad's power over me was absolute, but how much of that was real, and how much did I voluntarily give him? It certainly wasn't apples to apples with a supervisor at a job, of course. For all of the work Dad piled on me as a kid, I still had my own time, especially during summer break. I spent countless hours riding my bike to the library, or out in the country. That alone showed me that he didn't control one hundred percent of my life.

That thought led to another. How much of his own life did he control? I always thought of my dad as all-powerful, omnipotent, answering to no one, but of course that couldn't have been true. He always worked for someone else. My mom made a lot of the decisions on things at home. My dad's main areas of influence were managing the property and vehicles. And me.

And me.

He didn't have power over everything in our lives. He hardly had power over anything. I just couldn't see outside of our sphere far enough to realize what was happening. He needed something to control, some way to feel better about his own lack of power, and that something was me. And the more I resisted, the harder he tried. It was just the two of us, locked in a tiny, pointless, life-and-death struggle.

And because that was my life, my environment, my nurturing experience, I concluded that total domination of someone equaled value. That being the master of my universe was the only acceptable way to be. And as I moved forward in life, I was always at the bottom of the ladder, and I thought that meant that I was failing, that I had no value. But there's no personal value in power. I was longing for the wrong thing, and for the wrong reasons. Thank God I never became anyone's supervisor. The only real power I might have had would be to tell them what their job was, but my perception would've been that I needed to control their every thought and action, to own them, to dominate them, to force them to bend to my will. Just like my dad did to me.

I opened my eyes, and they happened upon the lamp in front of me. It had the power to brighten up the room, which was a function. While the light, or the lack of light, would certainly impact my life, it couldn't impact my value or my strength. And neither could another person. That wasn't how power worked.

"You look like you just discovered electricity," Nysa said with a grin. "What did you figure out?"

Energy and ideas were racing around my head, and I tried to channel it into something coherent. "I realized how much I've misunderstood everything, and how that's impacted my behavior for my entire life. I feel like I owe a lot of people an apology." I looked at my hands for a moment. "I thought that my dad's dominance over me was what gave him value, or status, or something. I equated his role as the judge, jury, and executioner to being the gold standard of adulting, and I couldn't seem to get there. But then I realized that he never got there either. The only thing he really had power over was me, and that clearly didn't bring him much satisfaction."

"Interesting." Nysa made a few notes. "What else?"

"That there will likely always be someone who has power over me in some way, but that doesn't have anything to do with who I am, or my value. Unless I end up in a POW camp getting tortured, there really isn't any way for anyone to impact my value or my strength. If someone else is creating a toxic power situation, like my dad did, it's about them and their issues, it's not about me. I'm solid."

"Spoken like a true prodigy," Nysa said with a smile. "We've processed this before, but let's do it again. What gives you value?"

Before I could answer, she turned the paddles back on. The familiar buzzing, left, right, left, right, was soothing as I shifted my focus from power to value.

I have value. It was something that had taken me years to really believe, and even now, I had moments when I would forget it. I had spent so many thousands of days believing that I had no value, nothing to contribute to the world, and feeling good about myself still seemed novel.

I have value. What gave me that value? I've written songs and recorded them. I've painted paintings that hung on the walls of our home, and in the homes of friends. I've written books, and my wife and I have a podcast that's helped people all over the world. Those things have brought both joy and knowledge to countless people. My wife entrusted me with everything in her whole world, from her finances and her business to her heart and soul. These things were my contribution to the world and to my wife, and that mattered, for sure. But there was something more.

What really made me feel good about myself was how I'd managed to stop the runaway train of my life. I broke the cycle of destruction, both for myself and the world around me. I became self-aware, and then I began to change, to grow, to become something better. I recognized my potential, and I challenged myself to grow into that potential. I stopped doing the same thing over and over, expecting different results. That gave me value.

I have value. My value didn't come from other people. And as such, it couldn't be taken away by other people. Value was just like happiness— it's an inside job.

"Where does your value come from?" Nysa asked, turning off the paddles.

I smiled. "It comes from who I am, my strength of character, my commitment to growth. It comes from my self-awareness. It comes from my contributions to the world, the satisfaction of making someone else's life better, even if only for a moment, through something that I was able to give them. It comes from me."

"You have value."

"I have value. And no one can take it away from me. It's impervious to power."

"And you believe way down deep inside that you have value."

"I do believe I have value. *And other things I wish I had known when I was a kid*, by Justin Long." I smiled, trying to let her know I wasn't beating myself up.

Instead of laughing, her face grew somber. "Why don't you spend some time with your five-year-old self and tell him about it? He's in your Pensieve, right? Exploring some exciting place?"

I nodded.

"That's your homework. Go talk to all the younger Justins in your Pensieve. Tell them how amazing they are, and how good life is because of them."

I left the office in a daze. My whole concept of how power worked had been turned on its head, and it was going to take me a while to regroup. It wasn't the first time, and it probably wasn't the last, but every time was important. These massive perspective shifts were changing my understanding of myself and what really shaped my world. Every time it happened, I felt better about me, both past me and present me. *That's* what I'd really been searching for my whole life. I just hadn't known where to look.

Chapter 13

CERBY TROTTED OVER TO ME as I sat down, and I scratched her ears for a moment while Nysa got settled in on the couch. For her part, Cerby showed more interest in sniffing my shoes than getting scratches, but that wasn't unreasonable.

Nysa gave it another minute, then sent the dog to her bed under the window. "We've got a lot of ground to cover today, Cerby. Go lie down." She pointed to the window, and the dog slunk away, glancing back at me over her shoulder as if to let me know she'd rather stay at my feet.

"Poor thing," I said. "Can't get no love."

"Yeah, yeah, my poor dog," Nysa laughed. "She's spoiled rotten. Okay, what are we working on today?"

"Conflict aversion," I answered. This was something I was more than ready to move past.

"That's right." She pulled out her notebook. "Tell me about it. What does conflict aversion mean to you?"

I'd been thinking about it for days leading up to my appointment, so I was ready for this one. "There are a couple of different ways it shows up for me. The first one is the people-pleaser aspect. I have a really hard time saying no when someone asks me to do something, so I end up doing a lot of things I don't want to do. Pretty straightforward."

Nysa smiled. "Yep. What else?"

"This one is a lot harder for me to grasp. I will fight with a boss, or my mother-in-law, or even my wife. Maybe not even fight, but just say nasty things, be a passive-aggressive, resentful asshole. But I'll never be rude to a stranger or someone more distant to me, like employees. I'm nice to our staff, no matter what. And I'm incapable of disciplining someone on the team or firing them. I can't do it. And that really bothers me because it's part of my job. So, I'm willing to be nasty to the people closest to me, and incapable of having a conversation that involves any kind of conflict with people outside of the inner circle."

Nysa wrote in silence for a minute, then looked up at me. "Have you ever tried to fire someone?"

"Yeah, once."

"What happened?"

I shook my head. "I couldn't do it. I practiced what I wanted to say, I coached myself, but when we were all in the office, I thought I was going to black out. My heart was pounding, my throat locked up, and I couldn't even speak. Fortunately, I had a contingency plan worked out with Erica, so all I had to do was tap her on the back, which I did, and she handled the meeting while I stood there and tried not to pass out."

"You were having an anxiety attack," Nysa said.

"It's not the first time, then," I said. "If that was an anxiety attack, then I've had several."

"What other time did you have one at work?"

"It was a few years ago," I said, shuddering. "There were these two ladies at the clinic picking up a horse that we'd done surgery on. There was some sort of misunderstanding about how much it was going to cost, and they were screaming at our office manager. It was like a reality show was being filmed in there. I walked in halfway through it and tried to settle the issue."

It was awful. I stood beside the desk in the tiny space, trying to be the firm but compassionate business owner. I was dizzy, and I couldn't seem to get enough air to keep up with my racing heart.

The women were being wildly irrational and inappropriate, taking turns shouting about what a scam this was. I was getting angry, which I knew was bad, but it also tempered the loss of oxygen with a massive adrenaline dump.

"And did you settle it?" Nysa asked.

"Yes, sort of. Once I understood the whole story, I could see where we might have done a better job managing expectations on cost, so I gave them a discount and walked out. I knew I was going to either pass out or lose my temper if I stayed any longer, so that was a lose-lose."

"So you were able to engage in conflict that time, but not very well."

"Well, it was already going on when I walked in, and I was mainly trying to end it to defend my employee, who was taking a lot of verbal abuse."

"Okay. Let's look at the other side. You said you don't have any problem being snippy to people close to you or people who have power over you, right?"

"Right. But I think those are two different things, maybe. Being rebellious to my bosses was about feeling controlled, which we worked on. I think arguing with my significant other, or her mother, is different."

"Okay, let's get into it." She unrolled the paddles and swung them over to me. "Start with the employee you tried to fire. Go back to that moment, and we'll see what comes up."

I closed my eyes as the paddles began to vibrate and forced a deep breath to calm myself.

Lisa had been an employee for three days when we decided we had to terminate her, but I had spent several months onboarding her. She'd been great in the interviews, had a ton of relevant experience, and I was really excited to have her as part of the team.

She had moved here for the job, which delayed her starting. We needed that time though, because we had just hired a new practice manager, and we had to get her settled in first. Lisa had wanted that management position, but I talked her into taking the office assistant position. Had I oversold her on what the job would be, or was I not as good at hiring as I thought I was?

We'd talked often during the weeks leading up to her start date. While a large part of the job was answering phones and making appointments, I'd focused on the other, more exciting stuff. I was all amped up about building a more active social media presence and increasing our community interaction and client education programs. I wanted her to be a big part of that. We also talked a lot about our culture and how important that was to us. Every person on the team was a critical part of that culture. The positive vibe was a big draw for her.

When she started, I stayed out of the office so she could focus on learning the basics. The computer program was new to her, and scheduling mobile veterinarians was not an easy process to learn, so I knew it would take some time for her to get her sea legs. But at the end of the third day, Amy, our new manager asked Erica and me for a meeting and explained that Lisa was not interested in being a team player.

"When I try to teach her a task, she shuts me down, and tells me that's not what she's here to do. She says she takes her orders from Justin and not me. She's being rude to everyone. We can't go another day like this."

I was stunned. What had happened? How had she been so amazing to me but so horrible to our team? I was completely responsible. I'd pushed hard to bring her on to the team. If she was a bad egg after all, what did that mean about me and my interview process?

"What's coming up?" Nysa asked.

My eyes fluttered open. "I haven't made it to the firing part yet. I was just going over what happened leading up to that. She was only there for three days, but she was a very different person then than she'd been leading up to her start date. But I think I'm figuring out where some of the anxiety is coming from."

"Yeah?"

I nodded. "I do this big, involved interview process. It's one of my pride points, and I've worked ridiculously hard to learn how to find really great people. And it's pretty solid. I've hired two bad apples in the last five years and about eight rock stars. One of the bad apples was a person we had misgivings about but settled on, which taught us a valuable lesson. The other one was Lisa. She seemed incredible in every way. Well, I say that, but I will admit that I had a twinge in my gut that I ignored."

"Why did you ignore it?"

"Because I thought I was being judgmental about something petty," I said. "Sometimes she talked slowly, like she was really choosing her words carefully when she would ask me questions about things. I told myself it was because she'd never worked in a vet clinic before and was nervous about how much she didn't know. She was in her fifties, and I wrote it off as her being worried about learning a lot of new stuff, but from her job history, I knew she would pick it up just fine."

"Is that where the anxiety is coming from? That you hadn't trusted your gut?"

I shook my head. "No, I took the fact that she made it through my character gauntlet as a sign that I don't actually know what I'm doing. I made a huge mistake by pushing her into a job that was an assistant to the job she applied for. Beyond that, I campaigned to her and to the rest of the team that this was the point when we were going to rocket into the next dimension. And it all blew up in my face. So I felt responsible for all the negativity they had to put up with for three days, which flies in the face of all the culture stuff I preach. And I felt like it was my responsibility to fire her, since I'd made this mess to begin with."

"What did you feel underneath the responsibility? What did you feel about yourself?"

It didn't take long to figure out. "I felt like a fraud. Here I was, this guy with a high school education who'd never even held a leadership position, and I was trying to run a business. I'd learned a lot about it and had enough success to think I was really doing it, but then this catastrophe hit."

Nysa wrote something down. "*I'm a fraud.* That's a good negative cognition. And what would you rather believe about yourself in that moment?"

"Anything!" I chuckled dryly. "I don't know. It's a complicated feeling. I spent all this time befriending her, and then I had to turn around and fire her. That made me feel like a fraud, too, like all the stuff I told her was a lie. It was as if I'd said, *I like you, I like you, I like you,* and then the next day, it's like, *Just kidding, I hate you, you're fired.* I couldn't make it work in my head. But it's complex, right? The situation changed. She changed."

Nysa was nodding. "Right. She didn't hold up her end of the bargain, and you had to react to that. So what do you think for a positive cognition? *I'm complex? Realistic?*"

"Let's go with that," I said. "It's not a straightforward relationship. There are a variety of factors. I have obligations, and I can't always be a people-pleaser in my position. It *is* complex."

"All right, let's rate it. One to ten, paired with firing Lisa, how disturbing is it to say, *I'm a fraud*?"

"Nine."

"One to seven, paired with firing Lisa, how true does it feel to say, *I'm complex?*"

"Two."

"Okay, you've got your cognitions. Let's go to the morning when you're going to fire her and see what comes up."

I saw her pull through the gate, right on time. My palms were sweaty, and while that was partly from nervousness, it was also shame. Why was I embarrassed? She was the one who had been acting inappropriately, not me. But here I was, feeling like I'd been caught stealing something.

I'm a fraud. Perhaps I focused our discussions on one particular aspect of the job, and she felt disillusioned by the mundane nature of the other tasks she was being asked to do. Even if that was the case, there was a right way to handle the situation, and refusing to listen to your supervisor wasn't it. She was behaving poorly. That had nothing to do with me. Her willingness to be defiant and rude right off the bat meant that she wasn't the kind of person we wanted on our team. She should be embarrassed about her behavior, but instead, I was ashamed about removing her from our team.

"What's coming up?" Nysa asked.

I opened my eyes slowly. "It's kind of weird, but I felt horrible about letting her go. She'd quit her old job and moved up here just for this, and here I was terminating her after three days. Logically it was the right call, but I have this crazy embarrassment thing attached to it. I didn't want to hurt her feelings or put her in a bad spot."

Nysa shifted on the couch. "Do you feel responsible for her feelings?"

"Yeah, I think so."

"How about the rest of your team? Are you responsible for protecting them from toxic people?"

My whole interview process existed to protect the clinic. I'd worked for a toxic person before, a supervisor who had to dominate everyone every minute of the day to feel like he had power and value. Someone a lot like my dad, actually. So I'd made it my mission to make sure people never dreaded coming to work at our vet clinic. Having a great culture of positivity and inclusivity was paramount to me. And what was I doing?

"Oh, my God," I said. The gears fell into place. "I'm protecting the bad apple instead of my team. Like everything else, I had it backwards." It was so obvious. How could I have failed to realize this? I wanted to crawl under a rock.

"You have a history of taking inappropriate responsibility for things," Nysa said. "It sounds like this is another manifestation of that."

I swallowed the shame in my throat and resolved to make this a growth opportunity instead of beating myself up. "That's exactly what it is. But I think I can use that feeling of embarrassment as a warning sign. Whenever I feel it, I need to take a second to see what I'm embarrassed about, and whether it's appropriate or not. I can totally fix this."

Nysa smiled. "Put that in your thought process, and let's get back into it. I want you to focus on what happened in the meeting, and what you were feeling."

The paddles came back on in my hands, and I closed my eyes. I was standing beside Erica, and slightly behind her. Amy was on the other side of Erica. Lisa stood in front of us, a look of confusion on her face. I tried to swallow, but my throat was closed. I knew what I wanted to say, but my body wasn't cooperating at all. The light in the room seemed to vanish around the edges, and the silence bore down like a weight as everyone waited for me to speak.

When I'd composed my termination statement, it started out filled with apologies. *Lisa, I'm so terribly sorry … Lisa, I feel horrible about this … You're a wonderful person and it rips my heart out to do this ….* Why was I so protective of her feelings? Recognizing those things as inappropriate for the situation, I'd removed them all, but here in the moment I was overwhelmed once again by the need to apologize to her. Perhaps my inability to speak was a good thing.

I'm a fraud. By firing her, I was reneging on our deal. And just maybe I was afraid that she would think poorly of me, that she would hate me. That felt even closer to the truth. Was I still so fragile in my sense of self that I needed everyone to like me? No. But I did spend most of my life in that head space. These feelings were a remnant of the old Justin, no longer relevant. They still popped up from time to time, and I'd failed to recognize them for what they were. That was good, though. That part of the problem was already solved, I just had to remind myself when necessary.

I'm complex. I *am* complex. The relationship I had with myself was complex, as were the relationships I had with others. To think that I could apply a simple yes/no to my relationship with another person, a good/bad, a binary, clear-cut definition, was unrealistic. It wasn't one factor being measured: yes or no. There were a hundred factors, a thousand, all moving and changing.

To change my mind about Lisa didn't mean that I was wrong or that I'd been wrong initially. It meant that enough of the factors had shifted to the *no* side of the line that our situation had changed. Changing my mind about Lisa didn't make me a bad person, it made me a good leader. It was the responsible thing to do. My responsibility to my team was paramount. Meeting that responsibility was complex. *I* was complex.

"Where are your thoughts?" Nysa asked.

I sighed. "Have I talked to you about Magrathea? It's a dead planet in *Hitchhiker's Guide to the Galaxy*."

Nysa shook her head. "No, but I'm familiar with it. What about it?"

I smiled in appreciation that she'd read one of my favorite series. "I use Magrathea as an analogy in AA meetings for the way my brain works. It's a good visualization tool. So, Magrathea was a dead planet. Its civilization had been extinct for millions of years. But before its inhabitants died out, they developed a missile defense system. It was all totally automated, solar powered, didn't need anyone to keep it running. Even though the people were long gone, the missiles still fired at a spaceship if it got too close. There was nothing to protect, but the automated system didn't know that, right? It was just doing what it had been programmed to do."

Nysa laughed, clapping her hands lightly. "I see where you're going with this."

"Right? That's what happened with Lisa. My automated system is programmed to think that I need her to like me so that I can like me. I was embarrassed about firing her because I was protecting myself. But none of that is relevant anymore. It's not necessary. I just didn't realize that's what was happening. The people-pleaser thing is part of my Magrathea missle system."

Nysa wrote some notes before glancing back up at me. "How does that play into you feeling like a fraud?"

I had to think about that for a minute. "I'm putting this together as I go, so bear with me."

"That's okay," Nysa said. "That's what we're doing here."

"I think that when I ask myself who I am, I picture my life as a whole. Justin from age six, from age twelve, from age seventeen, from age twenty-five, from age thirty-five. The vast majority of my life is the old Justin, the un-enlightened, broken, destructive Justin. That's what comes up automatically. Forty-four-year-old Justin is a completely different person, but it's such a recent part of my timeline that I forget to include it. Current Justin doesn't come up first in the search results. So when I think of myself as a fraud, it's because I'm putting my current activities against my skills and knowledge base from ten years ago, or fifteen, or whatever. I'm not a fraud, I'm just looking at a previous version of myself."

"I read a quote once that you might appreciate," Nysa said. "*Sometimes a hypocrite is nothing more than a person who is in the process of changing.*"

The statement rocked me. It was everything I was looking for, wrapped up in a single sentence. "That's perfect," I said at last. "I totally connect with that."

"I thought you might. Now then, let's do some more processing. I want you to go back to the meeting where you tried to fire Lisa and felt like a fraud and apply your Magrathea perspective to it. Think about how you would handle that meeting right this moment."

The paddles came back on. I took a deep breath, focusing on the sensation in my lungs and the calming effect on my mind, and let it out with control. Marshalling my intention, I closed my eyes and returned to the back office at the vet clinic.

My right hand discreetly tapped Erica on the back— our pre-arranged signal for her to take over. While she went through her process of terminating Lisa, I tried to see the situation through the eyes of forty-four-year-old Justin, the protector of the team, emotionally stable Justin, strong leader Justin, self-embracing Justin. Me. The sum of all my past selves and experiences. In this moment, how would I want current me to handle Lisa's termination?

I let the image of Erica speaking fade away, replacing it with a new one. In this new frame, I stepped forward, no longer hiding behind Erica. I stood in the center of the room, willing to be looked upon, thought about, observed, and judged. Willing to stand for what I believe in. Willing to do the right thing, even if it's hard. Willing to *be*.

I felt much calmer than before— nervous, perhaps, but nowhere near the realm of panic. I saw Lisa for what she was: a person, one whom I'd had a lot of hopes for, but who turned out to be wrong for our team. Not a bad person, not a reflection of me, just someone who we tried to work with, and it didn't pan out. If you try to put a puzzle piece into the wrong place, it damages the piece, as well as the other pieces around it. I was here to take that piece back off the board.

I swallowed easily, my throat in perfect working condition. "Lisa, we brought you here to try to strengthen our team and our culture, because those things are most important to us. You have demonstrated through your behavior and your attitude that you are not the right fit for this job. I'm sorry for the inconvenience this creates for you, but we're letting you go."

A pang of guilt shot through my stomach at the wounded look on her face. *Magrathea*, I whispered to myself. How she felt was not my responsibility. How I felt about myself had nothing to do with her. I was protecting our team.

A sense of satisfaction settled over me, as it always did when I learned to turn negative thoughts about myself into positive affirmations. While the process of growing could be painful, it was nothing compared to the agony of staying the same. I focused on the good feeling as the paddles buzzed in my palms, left, right, left, right, locking in the new perspective.

"How was it?" Nysa asked.

"Good." I smiled. "Really good. Hopefully, I'll never have to fire anyone else, but if it happens, I think I'll be able to do it. Now that I know how to interpret my feelings, I can see if they're appropriate or not."

Nysa began rolling up the cord, gently pulling the paddles out of my hands. "Fantastic! Let's do a final check-in on your cognitions, and we'll call it a day."

The excitement of new understanding was strong, but there was a hint of despair there, too, lurking in the shadows. Sometimes

I was overwhelmed by the number of things I'd been doing wrong all my life. I had to work at keeping a positive attitude. Yes, I'd spent a lot of years operating with backwards thinking, but playing the coulda-shoulda-woulda game with myself was pointless. The way forward was to view these things as growth opportunities. Each example I discovered was another way I could live a happier life from here on out.

My growth trajectory over twelve years of sobriety was remarkable to me in many ways, not the least of which was the seemingly endless layers of self that I'd gone through and worked on. In the beginning, each layer seemed to be the core when I discovered it. Now, a hundred layers in, I knew better. There was no core, no perfect center at which point nothing was left to fix. There would always be another layer, and that's a good thing. I'm at my best when I'm growing, and having nothing to work on would be terrible. For me, the thrill of self-discovery is what it's all about.

Chapter 14

I GLANCED AROUND NYSA'S OFFICE as I sat down, trying to absorb every element of it: the aura of healing, the mellow vibe, the safety that allowed me to bare my innermost soul. It was a good place. There were still two more sessions to go after this one, but I was already anticipating the loss of my weekly therapy, and I was sad about it.

This was a planned break. I'd processed a lot over our forty sessions, digging into my childhood and unearthing dozens of false beliefs about myself. The whole experience had been incredible, but I needed time to let it all marinate. I was afraid that if I didn't take some time off, I'd start forgetting some of the things I learned before they could get cemented in place.

Nysa grabbed my folder off the corner of her desk and plopped on the couch. "This thing is getting thick," she said, waving the sheaf of paper in the air. "We're going to have to start a second folder when you come back next spring."

I laughed. "You should see the inside of my head!"

"Oh, I know. That's why it's such a big deal to take a break once in a while." She opened the folder and glanced over the top few pages. "Are you ready to move on to your relationship with your mother?"

The thought of my mom was enough to disrupt the pH balance in my stomach. I had some work to do. "Yep, let's get into it."

"Okay. When you think about your mom, what feelings come to mind?"

A tsunami of thoughts, images, memories, and emotions swept through me in an instant. While my negative experiences with my dad had stopped when I moved out, things with my mother had continued accelerating, especially after my dad died. She was still alive, and while I had little to do with her these days, we still had occasional interactions. Our relationship was vastly different than what I'd had with my dad.

I'd been angry with my dad for controlling me so tightly, for crushing any self-confidence I might have developed. With my mom, it was different. I was ashamed of her. She had robbed me of my chance at a normal childhood with a loving mother and a sense of home. I hated her for being so broken, both physically and emotionally. I resented the way her ideas about things ended up with me being ostracized from my peer group.

At the other end of the room, Cerby let out a sigh, prompting me to take my own deep breath. "A lot of feelings come to mind. Disgust. A sense of loss."

Nysa looked up at me. "Loss. Elaborate."

"Loss, as in lost childhood. My dad did what he did, but I could have still had a semi-normal childhood experience if my mother had been a good mother. I feel like she robbed me of being a regular kid."

She grabbed the paddles and swung them over to me. "Okay, that might be a good negative cognition: *I missed out.* What's the positive cognition?"

I thought for a moment. "That I'm okay in spite of it. Regardless of her failures, I managed to get myself together."

"How about, *I'm okay regardless.* Does that feel right?"

"Yeah, I think so."

She wrote down some notes. "Okay, let's do some processing. Think about all the things she did that kept you from having a normal, happy childhood."

The paddles began buzzing in my palms, and I closed my eyes, leaning back into the chair. The lack of television was probably the first thing I'd realized as a kid. Everyone else had one, and we didn't. While I agreed with that decision as an adult, it made me feel different back then. When the other kids at school talked about the *Justice League*, or *Knight Rider*, I had no idea what they were talking about. I had almost no exposure to pop culture. When you're young, there's nothing more important than your social standing, and my mom was undermining mine.

Her extreme religiosity was another factor. She found a bible verse in 1 John 2:15-16 that she used as a blanket rejection of everything I liked.

Do not love the world or anything in the world. If anyone loves the world, the love of the Father is not in him. For everything in the world— the lust of the flesh, the lust of the eyes, and the pride of life— comes not from the Father but from the world.

Around the same time I was discovering rock and roll, she determined that all music that wasn't gospel music was "of the world" and therefore against God. There was even discussion about whether I could continue to be in the school choir. I was old enough then to know she was losing touch with reality, and sometimes I tried to find ways to use that to my advantage.

"Justin Boyd, turn that racket off!" My mom stood at the base of the stairs, shouting up at me.

She'd returned from the store faster than I anticipated, and I was caught blasting rock music. How could I turn this around?

I hit the power button and raced to the top of the stairs. "It's not racket, Mom. It's Christian rock." I was banking on her ignorance of modern music to sell the lie.

"It sounds like Satan music to me."

I shook my head. "It's Motley Crue. They're singing *Shout at the Devil.* It's like an exorcism song, when you shout at the demons to get out. They're just singing it in a way that kids today can get it. Lots of Christian bands are doing that. Bon Jovi, Guns and Roses, bands like that."

I could tell she was wavering, but I didn't want to oversell it. If she asked someone at church about it, I'd be sunk. Hopefully she'd believe me and just let it go.

"Well, it was way too loud, and I don't like it. And I'm sure you've got chores to be doing before your dad gets home."

She went back to the kitchen, and I sighed in relief. I was safe, at least for now.

Nysa stopped the paddles. "What's coming up?"

"A lot. Mostly old stuff, from when I was in grade school. There were her beliefs that kept me from having a regular childhood, and then there were some physical things that made me ashamed of her."

"Okay," Nysa said, grabbing her notebook. "Tell me about some of the beliefs first."

"There was the no-television or movies thing, the lack of exposure to pop culture."

"Yep, I remember that," Nysa said. "What else?"

"Oh, I almost forgot sports. I got to play soccer for a year or two when I was really young, like six or seven, but then I wasn't allowed to play sports anymore. It wasn't even that I was athletically inclined, but when all the other boys started playing baseball, or football, or basketball, I didn't. I never got to learn how to be on a team or develop that camaraderie that everyone else was getting."

"What was her reasoning with that?" Nysa asked.

I sighed, the old sense of exasperation rushing back, as if I'd just argued with my mother about it that morning instead of thirty-five years ago. "She was convinced I'd get hurt. She knew a guy at church who had broken his back and hurt his knee playing college football back in the early seventies, before I was even born. When my mom learned that's why he had a hard time getting around, she was sure that I'd break my back playing elementary school basketball, or whatever else I wanted to try."

"Okay, tell me about some other things."

"There was the religious stuff. She was so committed to it, and that really made me wonder about things as I got closer to being a teenager. According to her, God would solve all our problems if we prayed hard enough and gave our hearts to him. But nothing ever changed. We were always poor, my dad was always angry, and my mom was always distressed."

I took a breath, forcing my shoulders to relax. "And when she got into the historical reenactment thing and decided she was a Cherokee medicine woman, it got even worse. She still did the church thing, but then she had to do all this other ceremonial stuff, too, burning sage, wearing a medicine pouch around her neck, all that. And, being my mother, she learned to speak and write Cherokee and made all her clothes to fit the role, and all that. Picture my mom sitting in the second row at church, a crazy white woman in full Cherokee garb, fully expecting Jesus to perform a miracle any minute."

Nysa giggled. "I'm sorry, I don't mean to laugh, but it's a pretty far-out-there mental image."

I waved my hand. "No, I get it. It looked ridiculous. It *was* ridiculous. I knew that. Hell, everyone knew that but her. And my dad sat right beside her in his ribbon shirt and overalls, daring anyone to say something. You talk about robbing me of a normal childhood. That alone would have been enough to do the job."

"For sure," Nysa agreed, jotting down some notes. "Was that the physical stuff you were talking about? Your mom's clothing choices?"

"Oh, no. This was way worse than that, in some ways. Kids are cruel, right? Brutal. My mom had scoliosis or something similar when she was young, and it messed up her spine. They did surgery and put in a metal framework to support her, which made her back a big, misshapen lump. Of course, once the kids at school saw her, she became a hunchback to them. If she'd been popular with them, maybe they wouldn't have turned on her like that, but she was the one that wouldn't let me watch movies, and made me wear clothes from Goodwill, and all that."

"Yeah, it snowballs," Nysa said. "What else?"

I debated about not mentioning the IBS because it was gross

and demeaning in a way. But it had happened, and it was a factor in my resentment against her. It had to be discussed.

"Remember that I was a little kid," I said. "I didn't understand things then the way I do now."

"You don't have to qualify things," Nysa said. "But go on."

I shifted in the chair, trying to find a way to phrase it that didn't feel so awkward. "So, my mom has IBS," I finally said. "She always has. There wasn't a name for it back then, so she thought she was allergic to everything, or that she got the nervous poops when she was stressed out. Anyway, she would have diarrhea all the time. And not always in the bathroom."

Nysa raised an eyebrow. "As in, whoops?"

"Exactly. Usually in the van when we were headed somewhere. That was way better than it happening once we got there, for sure, but it stunk so bad. And my dad would turn around in the passenger seat, since my mom always drove, and give me the savage face if I dared to make a sound. So we would turn around and drive home, all the while pretending nothing was happening. It was horrible."

"Did it happen a lot?"

"I don't know. Probably only a couple of times, but there were a lot of false alarms with bad gas, and I lived in terror of it happening in public. I didn't know how to separate her shame from my shame."

Nysa wrote for nearly a minute before speaking. "Okay. I think we're getting a better picture of things. Let's check in on our cognitions before we move on. Paired with your mom robbing you of a normal childhood, how disturbing is it to say, *I missed out*?"

"Ten."

"And paired with the lost childhood, how true does it feel to say, *I'm okay regardless*?"

I hesitated. While I knew I had overcome these hurdles, I was still missing out on the family experience as an adult, and the sense of loss persisted. "Two."

"Let's go back in. Now I want you to think about the current timeframe. When you think about your mother today, right now, what feelings do you have?"

The paddles began buzzing again, and I brought an image of my mom to the front of my mind. The last time I had seen her was when Erica and I got married in 2015, five years earlier. I had set aside all my issues with her and tried to create a family moment. I flew her out to Florida, with my sister acting as chaperone to keep her from getting lost in the airport.

I pictured her sitting on the couch in our living room as Erica and I worked on our costumes for the wedding. We'd decided to have a costume wedding. Erica was dressing as Laura Croft, Tomb Raider. I was King Arthur, from Monty Python and the Search for the Holy Grail. It wasn't going to be a religious ceremony, and I knew my mother was biting her tongue about that. Her agreement to not preach to us about anything had been my main requirement in allowing her to attend.

She was much older than my mental image of her. She sat there silently, and I felt like she was making the point that if she couldn't talk about Jesus, then she had nothing to say. I was seven years sober then, and my interactions with her had become fewer and farther between as the years passed. I had changed so much, and I was hoping that she had, too, but we were strangers with no central ground to meet upon.

The longer she was there, the clearer it became that she was just as sick as she'd ever been. It wasn't that she did or said anything. Instead, she was trying not to cause a scene, so she *didn't* do or say anything. It was the first time Mom had met Erica, but she didn't make any effort to get to know her at all. I felt obligated to explain to everyone that she was just nervous and wasn't being stand-offish. She clearly felt terribly out of place and didn't know how to handle it.

What did I feel? I was getting better by leaps and bounds, but she was still waiting on Jesus to fix her. I felt angry, disappointed, robbed yet again. She'd listened over the years of my recovery from alcoholism to what I was doing to turn my life around. I'd told her the things I was learning in counseling. There was a way out for her, and I gave her all the resources I had, and yet she refused to use them. Yes, I felt angry with her. Furious. If she had followed me in a new direction, we could be having a wonderful time. Instead, I regretted bringing her into my home and introducing her to my wife and friends. I was still ashamed of her.

"What's coming up?" Nysa asked.

"I'm angry at her," I said. "Furious. As soon as I think about her, I get mad."

"Why? What are you mad about?"

"Because she won't fix herself," I said. There was an edge to my voice, and I took a deep breath before continuing. "She knows she's got emotional problems. We talked about it ad nauseum back when I used to talk to her. We've compared notes on feelings and self-beliefs, and all of that. The first time I went through counseling, and really starting learning who I am, I was excited to share my growth with her. I tried to talk her into therapy. I showed her the results, the proof that there was hope for her. And yet, here we are, ten years later. She won't do anything to change except pray harder and find a new church when the current one proves to be a bust."

My chest was heaving, and I could feel my pulse in my temples. I sucked in as much air as I could hold through my nose and held it for a ten-count. As I let it out, my shoulders dropped a few inches. I hated that I was still carrying so much rage around.

"Do you think she's capable of changing?" Nysa asked once my breathing was under control.

"Oh, I'm sure she is," I said. "She's just as smart as I am."

"But she hasn't ever done anything except pursue a spiritual solution, right?"

I started to reply, but her point struck me mute. *Was* she capable of changing? At seventy years old, she was running out of time. Perhaps intellect wasn't a good way to gauge her capacity to change. "I guess maybe I don't know if she's capable," I said slowly. "I've always looked at her religious determination as something she could redirect at therapy, but maybe not."

"Justin, if she could do what you're doing, she would've done it." Nysa smiled sadly. "She's stuck on her path, and there's nothing you can do about it. You showed her your path, and gave her directions, but if she doesn't do it, that's it. You can't force her to change. You can't make anyone change, and it's not your responsibility. You did your part, and you have to find a way to accept the situation for what it is. She might never get it, and that's sad, but you can't do anything about that. But you can't be angry at her forever, either."

I nodded in silence. An analogy was forming in my imagination, a way to visualize the situation. It was something that Roland had taught me to do when struggling to accept something, and I'd found it to be an incredibly useful tool.

"Okay, hear me out," I said. "I'm working this out as I go, sort of a visualization thing."

"Go ahead," Nysa said. "Do you want the paddles on?"

"Yeah, that would be great." I leaned back and stared into the lamp. "I'm picturing myself out in the ocean on a boat, a big sailboat. Like a yacht. I didn't start out there, but I've worked my way up to the yacht from a piece of driftwood. If I look over the railing on one side, I can see my mom out in the water. She's clutching a board, bobbing around, exhausted, and every once in a while, a wave crashes over her. She's sputtering for air, flailing, and sometimes she goes under for a few seconds. I've tried everything in the world to save her. I've thrown life ring after life ring to her, rowed out there in the dinghy to get her, tried to tie a rope around her to haul her in, but she won't let go of the driftwood. She's going to drown out there, right beside my yacht, for no goddamned reason, and that's what makes me angry. The fact that it's so completely avoidable and senseless." I realized I was shouting, and my mouth snapped shut.

"What are you going to do?" Nysa asked softly.

I threw my hands up, and they crashed back into my lap as the only possible path became clear. My eyes filled with tears, and I struggled to find a different answer, but I kept coming to the same conclusion. "I have to let her go," I whispered weakly. My voice cracked. "What else can I do? I have to let her go." The tears spilled silently down my cheeks.

I stood at the rail of the boat, looking out at my mom. She was bobbing up and down with the waves, ignoring all the life rings floating around her, and I knew that one day she would slip beneath the surface and never come up again. It wasn't my fault, and I really believed that, but it was incredibly difficult to watch her do it. I let out a shuddering breath and began pulling in the life rings, one by one. I drew the dinghy back on board with the crane and set it in the cradle. It wouldn't do for my lifeboat to be out there if I needed it here. When I was done, I looked back at my mother. Nothing had changed. I was no longer deploying my resources to her, but it was still difficult to see her there.

I took the proffered tissue from Nysa and blew my nose. My face felt swollen.

"Where are you?" Nysa asked.

I shrugged and stared at my hands. "Trying to figure out what to do. I can't just stand here and look at her. It sounds callous, but I feel like I ought to build a wall or something so I can't see her."

"That's not going to work," Nysa said. "She's still going to be a part of your life in some way. Pretending she doesn't exist will just make it harder when those interactions happen."

I shook my head. "You're right, you're right. I'm just scrambling here, trying to find a solution." I blew my nose again and let out a deep sigh. My rage had drained away, leaving me ragged and disheveled. "I guess I just have to figure out how to accept that she's going to be there, and keep living my life the best I can."

Nysa nodded with a sad smile. "That's all you can do, Justin. You just keep living your best life. She can see you, and she knows where the boat is. Maybe someday she'll change her mind and ask for a lifeboat, and maybe she won't. Either way, you're going to be okay."

"I'm going to be okay," I repeated. "That's right. I *am* okay, and I will continue to be okay. She's going to do what she's going to do, and I can be sad that she's suffering, but it's not my business, not my responsibility."

"That's right," Nysa said. "Your responsibility is to take care of you. You're doing that. Right?"

"I am," I said.

"Your mom wasn't capable of being the mother you needed when you were a child, and she's still not. But that's okay. You get to choose people to have in your life that do provide the emotional interactions that you need. *You are okay*. You didn't just survive the driftwood you were stuck on as a child. You collected other pieces of wood and slowly turned it into a giant sailboat. That's huge! Can you see that?"

"Yes." I cleared my throat and tried again. "Yes, I can see it."

"Let's check in on your cognitions. Paired with your mom robbing you of a normal childhood, how disturbing is it to say, *I missed out*? One to ten."

I did miss out. I missed out on a lot of things. But the fact that my experience was different from other people's doesn't mean anything. If I hadn't started out in such a bad place, I never would've ended up where I was now, and that would be a tragedy. My life today was wonderful, and I had a lot of not-so-wonderful experiences to compare it to, so there's no doubt. Yes, I missed out on some things, but I gained other things, and I wasn't going to be angry about it. After all, I wasn't the one still stuck on a piece of driftwood.

"Two."

"And one to seven, paired with the lost childhood, how true does it feel to say, *I'm okay regardless*?"

"Seven."

Nysa jotted down my answer and began rolling up the paddles.

I felt completely drained, as if I had been wrung out like a dishrag. "Is it me, or did we just get run over by a bulldozer?" I asked. "I feel like I got flattened."

"You just did some monster processing. You ought to sleep

well tonight."

I hoped she was right, but the image of my mom hanging on the driftwood stayed with me. I had a better perspective on things, but it was going to take time to get used to seeing her there without feeling the kneejerk reaction of anger or the need to rescue her.

The more I thought about it, the clearer it became that it wasn't just about my mom. I tried to fix everyone around me. Sometimes people asked for my help, but a lot of them hadn't. It might be hard to watch people suffer, especially when I can see so clearly how to solve their issue, but it wasn't my place to try to change them. An old saying from AA came to mind: *Acceptance is the answer to all my problems.* That might not be completely true, but it was perfect for this situation. If I could accept my mom and everyone else, instead of trying to fix them, I would have much more peace in my life.

Chapter 15

"We've got the last two sessions to talk about the death of your dad." Nysa sat on the couch with her bare feet curled up beneath her. "Lots of time. Let's start with what happened, and when, and where you were at in your life at that point."

"Okay." I settled into my chair and took a deep breath. "That was December of 2004. December sixteenth, which was about three weeks after I turned twenty-nine. I was still drinking then—I didn't get sober until February of 2008. I had just started working on Fort Stewart as a civilian contractor that September, I think. Is that right? I'm trying to get all the puzzle pieces on the board."

"Take your time," Nysa said.

"I think that's right," I continued. "I went to Iraq as a civilian contractor in December of 2003, and I came home in May of 2004. I sat around and drank beer for a few months, and then I got the job on the army base. And right after that, my dad got killed in a car wreck. That's right."

It had been a long time since I thought about that stuff, and a lot of the memories were covered in sediment.

"You went to Iraq as a civilian contractor?"

I nodded. "Yeah, it was right after the invasion. You could make eighty thousand dollars a year, tax free. Back then, that was the same as telling me I could make a million bucks. It seemed like a lot of money."

"What did you do?"

"I drove a truck. Well, that's not even true, not really. I rode around in the passenger seat of a truck. We were driving these big heavy equipment haulers, moving tanks and vehicles in and out of Iraq and Kuwait. There were two guys on a team. My partner liked driving, and I liked drinking and taking pictures, so I really didn't even do much work other than chaining and unchaining the loads."

"You could drink there?"

I laughed. "Not officially, no. It was a firing offense, but a lot of us did it anyway, even the supervisors."

"How did you get it?"

Now that I was digging them up, memories came flooding back. The flies, the heat, the noise of the trucks, the dust, the boredom, it was all still there. And the excitement of buying whiskey.

"There were specific routes that the military convoys used, and in certain places, we would have to slow down to a crawl to negotiate a tight turn. The locals used these places to their advantage, and came out to sell stuff to us. You could buy alcohol, cigarettes, hash, bootleg movies, porn, that kind of stuff. Kids would run up to the trucks, and we'd lean out and give them five or ten bucks and grab the goods. People would throw food to the kids too, which was a big no-no, because sometimes the wind would catch it and blow it into the road, and a kid would get run over trying to get to it. But anyway, that's how we got booze."

"Kids were selling it on the side of the road?" Nysa looked horrified, and I suppressed a smile.

The shock I had felt in the beginning of seeing five-year-old kids selling booze, smokes, and porn was quickly replaced by a sense of normalcy, and that was my marketplace for five months. "The kids were the runners. There would be a guy standing behind a pickup truck nearby— he was the one selling it. The kids would give him the money from their last sale, and he would give them something else to go hawk. It was a pretty genius system, really."

"Except when a kid got run over."

My face fell. "Yeah, except for that."

"Okay, we're getting way off track. But it's important to know that you risked your life and your job to drink in an active war zone. For now, let's get back to your dad. You were working in a new job?"

"Yeah. But one more important rabbit hole. That summer, after I came home from Iraq, we went to Oklahoma to spend a couple of weeks with my family. It was a really nice time, and without a doubt the best two-week period I ever spent around my dad. We didn't argue a single time. I didn't drink a lot, just enough to stay in my happy place. But I went home feeling like we'd made it to a new level in our relationship. I didn't quite get approval, but I didn't get disapproval, and that was a big deal."

"What did you want approval for?"

"Going to Iraq," I said. "I went to Kuwait when I was in the army, but that didn't seem to impress him. I was hoping that charging into a hot zone would get his attention, even though I did it as a civilian instead of a soldier. I really wanted him to see me as an adult, a man, an equal. Someone worth acknowledging."

Nysa was writing furiously on her notepad, and I waited for her to catch up before continuing.

"The visit was in July, because we were there for the fourth. My brother and I shot fireworks off the dock for everyone at the lake. That was also weird, in a way. My dad never let us have any kind of fireworks when I was a kid. Not even sparklers. It was just another sign of how much he changed after I left."

"Did that hurt your feelings?"

I nodded. "In a way. I think it made me jealous of my brother, but mostly it just hurt that he had waited so long to loosen up and be a normal dad."

"Got it. Go on."

"That was the last time I saw my dad, or even talked to him, I think. I'm not positive about that part, but we never talked on the phone much. Six months later, he was on his way home from work over in Bartlesville, probably an hour's drive. Halfway there, out in the middle of nowhere, he drifted off the edge of the road.

He over-corrected when he jerked the wheel, trying to get the tires back up on the asphalt, and he ended up in the oncoming lane and had a head-on collision with a pickup. He died on the spot."

Nysa handed me the paddles. "Let's get into that night. Think about what happened, and what you were feeling. Just go with your thoughts. And remember to take Dr. Who with you, and Bob Ross. You can lean on them any time you need to."

The paddles began buzzing in my palms, left, right, left, right. I pulled a deep breath in through my nose and let it out with a sigh, relaxing my shoulders.

I remembered my mom calling in the middle of the night. It was late, probably close to midnight, even though the wreck had occurred hours before. I woke up, confused by the sound of the ringing phone.

"Hello?"

The caller ID told me it was my mom's number, which was the only way I knew it was her on the other end. The voice I heard then sounded foreign to me, it was the voice of an old, old woman, shaky and weak, barely audible.

"Son?" Her voice was a coarse whisper, rough but nearly transparent.

"Yeah?"

Silence on the line for a moment.

"Is Kari there with you?"

"Yeah. What's going on?"

More silence, accentuated by heavy breathing. "Are you sitting down?"

I found myself getting irritated with her. Obviously, something was wrong, and I just wanted her to get to the point. "Yes," I lied. I was standing in the living room. Kari waited in the doorway behind me, a puzzled look on her face. I repeated the question more forcefully this time. "What's going on?"

Another long moment passed in silence, broken only by the sound of breathing through the phone. "Your— your dad had an accident on the way home this afternoon."

I wasn't alarmed. The first thought I had was that he'd broken his leg, and they were going to need me to send money to keep them afloat for a bit. They would certainly need some money to fix the car. It was an old '70s station wagon, and my dad would comb through junkyards to find the pieces he needed to get it functional again. I was so certain of this that I nearly asked how the car was before inquiring about my dad. Very nearly.

"Is he okay?"

My mother burst into hysterical sobbing, the same kind she had done for hours on that day out in Wyoming when she wanted so desperately to die.

A faint alarm bell was dinging in the back of my mind, but I still wasn't prepared for her eventual answer.

"He— he didn't make it." Her voice shuddered, thin and shaky, yet laced with the strength of abject terror. "He's dead."

"What?" I asked, staring at the wall in confusion. There was no answer, just incessant sobbing on the other end. "What?"

Kari walked over into my field of view. "What's going on?" she mouthed.

"My dad got killed in a car wreck," I said. The words coming out of my mouth seemed to be at a distance, as if someone else was saying them. I sat down on the sofa abruptly, too stunned to make sense of anything. My mother was gasping for air, making sounds that made me want to hang up the phone. "Do you want me to come home? What am I saying? Of course I'm coming. Let me figure out what I'm doing."

Kari sat down beside me. I felt strange, as if I should be feeling something specific, but I didn't know what. It had been a normal night for a weekday, so I'd only had six or seven beers before supper. That was good, as I was struggling to process the information, and had I been drunk, it would have been even worse.

"Tell me what you were feeling," Nysa said, shutting the paddles off. "In that first moment, sitting on the couch."

I closed my eyes and focused on the memory. It was hard to get past the dumb shock. There were traces of other things beneath it, glimpses of conflicting emotions. There was the feeling that I'd been hit in the stomach with a baseball bat, but I was also oddly grateful that our last interaction had been a good one, that for once I didn't have to regret something.

"It was really convoluted," I said at last. "Disbelief. Horror. Fear."

"What were you afraid of?" Nysa asked gently.

What was I afraid of? "I'm not sure. Maybe the permanence of it? Like, it can't be undone. I've always had a fear of things like that. It's my low risk tolerance. I don't like not being able to change my mind, to be stuck forever with no options to undo. I can't function without Control Z."

Nysa gave me a puzzled look. "What does that mean?"

"It's the keyboard command to undo on a computer."

She rolled her eyes theatrically. "Okay. What else were you feeling?"

I went back to the couch in the house on First Street in Hinesville. So much of my life happened in that house. We lived there for eight years, the last eight years of my drinking. All the bad stuff happened there. Good things, too, of course, but it doesn't take a lot of mud to spoil a nice painting, and I had kicked up a lot of mud. But at that moment, Kari and I came together in the crisis.

Kari sat down beside me on the couch, her face the picture of concern. "What happened? I don't understand. We were just there."

Her sleepy confusion matched my own. People had died before, but no one very close to me. I had no concept of how to handle it. I knew I should've felt grief, but all I could feel was shock and emptiness.

"He was on his way home from work, and he got killed in a wreck. That's all I know. I could barely understand her."

While most of my mind was locked down trying to grasp this new development, a piece of it was slinging thoughts around in a blur. How fast could you get plane tickets these days? 9/11 had been only a few years before that, so there were a lot of unknowns. What was my mom going to do for income? My dad had always been the one with a job. And did a tiny, tiny part of me feel some sort of satisfaction? I slammed the door on that. No, of course not. That would be ridiculous. We had our issues, but I never wanted him to be *dead.* Right?

I opened my eyes and glanced at Nysa. "I think I was afraid of feeling vindicated, but some part of my brain was trying to tell me this was justice. Just thinking that made me feel horrible, like I was some kind of patricidal sociopath. Even then, I couldn't allow myself to wish any ill on my parents. I think I still believed we were going to put the past in the past and be a real family eventually, especially after our visit that summer."

"Were you involved with them? I mean, I know you went there that summer, but was that the first time you'd gone back?"

"No, I went back all the time, at least every other year. Is that crazy? I got out, but then I kept going back. I called them all the time, too, but I always had a buzz when I did. And I sent them money for various things. Our relationship was a whole lot better when there were a thousand miles between us, and I guess I never actually considered cutting them out of my life completely. I had this sense of obligation to them because we were related, and that got even stronger after my dad died. I didn't break that concept until I was two years sober."

"What happened to change your ideas on that?"

Images flooded through my mind, memories of countless hours sitting at Roland's house talking about all the baggage I was carrying around. That was the beginning of my journey to self-awareness, and every day was a growth spurt. And like all growing, some of it was painful. "Roland, my mentor, gave me a wonderful gift. He told me that the only one who could obligate me to another person was me. That was freeing in a way that I couldn't even begin to explain. He gave me permission to make an honest appraisal of my relationship with my family. When I did, I realized that I wasn't getting anything positive out of it at all, and I was dumping money and emotional expectations into a hole that couldn't be filled."

Nysa smiled. "And what did you do with that?"

"I shut off the money. And I stopped calling. And guess what? They all survived. I wasn't saving the day anymore, but somehow, they all kept making it through life. And little by little, they stopped calling too, and we drifted apart."

"Imagine that," she said.

"Imagine that," I agreed. "That cut a lot of stress out of my life. Understanding that I didn't owe my mother anything just because she birthed me was huge. It was like I'd been tied to a crazy animal for years, and one day I realized that I wasn't tied at all, I was just holding on to the rope. So I let go."

Nysa smiled again, the tiny diamond in her lip flashing in the lamp light. "Okay, let's get back to the day your dad died. You felt guilty for some of the thoughts you had." She paused and looked over her notes. "What happened when you got to Oklahoma?"

A lot of that time was blur. We flew out the following morning and landed in Tulsa, where we rented a car. Pawhuska was an hour drive north from the airport. Somewhere in the middle, out in the rolling hills and pastures, I had to pull over. We were only thirty minutes away, and I couldn't avoid thinking about it any longer. I imagined my dad lying in a casket, and that prompted a childhood memory that brought the first of many tears.

"Are you okay?" Kari asked as I whipped the car onto the shoulder. There was no other traffic out here, but I fumbled for the emergency flashers anyway. My vision blurred before I could find the button in the unfamiliar rental car, and I gave up as sobs wracked my chest. I couldn't answer her. I could barely breathe.

The memory was from the '80's, back in the time of the trash can and the ditch digging. My mom and dad were on the porch swing, and I sat on the front step, a rare night of just hanging out. My mom was humming "The Old Rugged Cross," a song from church.

"That's the song I want sung at my funeral," my dad said.

The thought of my dad dying made me burst into tears. He couldn't die. If anyone should die, it should be me, not him. I was the one who couldn't do anything right. How deeply I believed in his infallibility. How thoroughly I was convinced that he was right, and I was wrong. That moment burned itself into my memory, and I thought of it every time I heard the song. And then, when he really did die, it completely hijacked my mind and tried to destroy me.

We sat on the side of the road, the dead yellow grass of the Oklahoma winter stretching to the gray horizon. It hurt to cry. It was physically painful, and I was surprised at that, maybe even slightly alarmed. I hadn't cried in many years, other than a lone tear at the occasional sad movie. This was different. It was a deep, full-body anguish that threatened to make me black out. My throat hurt as my body tried to remember how to cry, muscles long atrophied being called upon to perform. I was vaguely aware that Kari put the transmission in park, but I was unable to express my gratitude with more than a vague fluttering of my hand.

It lasted about five minutes. The hoarse wretched sounds I was making sounded foreign, unlike anything I'd ever done before. While my body was trying to tear itself apart, my mind was showing me a replay of every moment I'd spent loathing my dad, hating him with every fiber of my being. I was overwhelmed by guilt and devastated that I'd never have a chance to apologize to him, to try and make things right for all the grief I'd caused him. For disappointing him. For not being a better son. Regret. I was filled with regret.

When it tapered off, I felt exhausted, emotionally drained, but better. I blew my nose on a tissue from Kari's purse and wiped my eyes on my sleeves.

"Sorry about that," I mumbled, embarrassed at the scene I had created. "I guess it all caught up to me."

Kari looked at me as if I were crazy. "That's not something to be sorry for, Justin. Your dad just died. This is a big deal. It's okay to cry. You need to let it out."

I didn't press the issue. The road behind us was empty, and I eased back onto the blacktop. We tried listening to the radio, but everything grated on my nerves, and I shut it off after a few minutes. What kind of music would be appropriate for this trip? We didn't stop again until we got to Pawhuska, where I went straight to the liquor store. I bought a half-gallon of whiskey and a couple cases of beer, and Kari got a bottle of rum. Then we went down the street to my parents' house.

I don't know what I was expecting. I guess I thought my brother and sister would be the only ones there, aside from my mother. Instead, the street was lined with cars. Some of my aunts and uncles were in the yard, along with my cousins, clustered in small groups. From the vehicles parked down the street, I could surmise that others were inside, along with my grandparents. I had to fight off the overwhelming urge to turn around and leave. I clenched the wheel, and Kari put a hand on my arm to soothe me.

Instead of turning around, I parked. Adam, my cousin that I'd lived with years before, met me at the car and wrapped me up in a hug. That brought on my second round of tears, and while it hurt, it wasn't as bad as the first one. It was cathartic, and again, I felt better once I got it out. Before I went up the driveway to see the others, I slipped behind the open trunk lid and swallowed some whiskey straight from the bottle.

"Let's pause there," Nysa said, drawing me back to the present. "You've mentioned before that your drinking in the aftermath of your dad's death is something that you really feel guilty about, right?"

I nodded silently.

"Okay," she continued. "That's been covered. We processed shame of behavior already. I want to separate the trauma of your dad dying from the trauma of your behavior in the weeks that followed. They're two different things. Does that make sense?"

"Yeah, I understand that. When I think of it as a whole, the shame of behavior tends to eclipse everything else. It'll be good to zoom in on the specific elements."

"Right. So leading up to this, you had the summer visit where things went well. I'm glad that happened because it gives us a positive point to look at. Let's focus on that for a minute." She paused long enough to grab the paddles, then resumed as she unwound the wires and swung them over to me. "Think about that trip and what you were feeling with your dad."

The paddles began buzzing in my hands, left, right, left, right, and I let my mind drift back to July of 2004. We had stayed in an RV out at the lake, a small camper owned by my sister's boss. It was right on the water with a swimming dock, which we used regularly. Adam and his family came out a few times, as did my family. There was food, laughter, and a lot of time spent watching the kids swim.

My dad was like a stranger. Everyone was a stranger, really. I'd changed over the ten years I'd been gone, but despite my intermittent visits, it never occurred to me that time would go by for them, too. There were more gray hairs in his beard and hair than ever before. He used a cane now, too, but that wasn't the thing that felt so strange. I finally realized what it was as the family gathered at the lake to shoot off fireworks.

My dad sat in an old lawn chair across the fire ring. My sister's son, still a toddler, was running around playing with rocks and sticks. I found his endless noise and energy irritating, and that's what made me realize what was so different about my dad. He was smiling. The kid was being a kid, and my dad was enjoying it.

I knew my dad was getting more mellow over the years, but that moment really made me understand just how different my experience with him had been. My dad didn't smile in any of my memories, with very few exceptions. Instead, he was nearly always angry, or at least irritable. Had he used it all up on me?

Nysa shut the paddles off, and I took a moment to collect myself. "I'd never seen my dad so laid back, maybe even happy. I convinced myself that me being gone was the primary driver for that, although I'm sure that age was a factor as well."

"Give me an example," Nysa said.

"Okay, here's a good one. We did a cookout at the lake. Kari and I were trying not to drink openly in front of them, although I had a beer or two with supper. She had her rum and coke in a Styrofoam cup from the gas station with a lid on it. We were sitting around the fire after we ate, and my sister's kid was wandering around. I think he was two or three. Anyway, he picked up her cup and started to take a sip out of it, and Kari was like, 'No, no, no, that's not for you, kiddo.' My mom said it was okay, since he was learning to drink out of a straw, so Kari had to tell them it had rum in it. Instead of being taken aback, everyone had a good laugh about it. My mom probably didn't find it that funny, but my dad thought it was hilarious. So that was one."

Nysa smiled. "In a situation where he would have responded with anger at another time in his life, he was able to laugh."

"Right. That same trip, we were at their house. My dad said something to my brother, although I can't remember what it was. My brother, I think he was about seventeen then, replied with some wisecrack and blew him off. I was stunned that he had the nerve to say it, and then my dad just sat there at the table and acted like nothing happened. I freaked out a little bit, I guess. I asked my dad if he was just going to let that go, because I would have gotten my ass kicked for saying something like that. He just shrugged, and that was the end of it."

"How did that make you feel?" Nysa asked.

I closed my eyes and reached back, opening myself to the emotions of the incident. My clenching fists were a good sign that I was getting dialed in. "It was bullshit. Either my dad was wrong for the way he treated me, or he was wrong for the way he was treating my brother, because they were incongruous. It wasn't fair. So maybe I wanted my brother to suffer the same way I did. Or maybe I wanted my dad to acknowledge that he'd been too hard on me. To apologize for something. To admit that he'd been wrong."

"Okay, but how did that make you feel?" Nysa repeated.

My nails dug into my palms. "Angry. Wronged. Openly dismissed. Insulted. Like my experience didn't matter." An analogy popped into my head. "If my dad had sold me something for a thousand dollars, and then sold the same thing to my brother ten years later for fifty bucks, that's how I would've felt. Like he was screwing me over right to my face."

"Now let's go back to the fire by the lake," Nysa said. "None of those things happened there, right? It seems like your dad accepted you, even with the drinking. Go back to the moment and focus on that."

The paddles came back on, calming me. I closed my eyes with a sigh and went back to the lake. I sat in a folding camp chair next to Kari. Across the fire, my mom and dad sat in old, mismatched lawn chairs. I watched as the baby grabbed Kari's cup, and I looked at my dad as he grinned. His beard, always so dark in the past, was mostly white, as was his long hair. He looked so familiar, yet at the same time, a stranger. He was doing nothing to me, nothing negative at all, but that wasn't enough to stop the stab of anger in my heart when I looked at him. Anger, and if I focused on it for a moment, it could easily become rage. He sat there, smiling, and I hated him. I didn't know any other way to feel about him.

I opened my eyes and looked at Nysa with a dawning realization. "It's not about him accepting me, not now. I agree that it probably happened for him. But I don't know how to accept *him*. I've never accepted him. Maybe he got past that, but I don't think I ever did. My whole existence was wrapped around my search for his acceptance and approval, but it never occurred to me that I couldn't accept him. I only know how to resent him." My nose began burning, a moment of notice before the tears came. I fell silent and let the blackness consume me.

The tension in my chest was building, and my thoughts grew sluggish. I was still filled with rage, even now, sixteen years after his death. All my life, he had been the epitome of consistency when disciplining me, never missing an opportunity to correct me. I could acknowledge that his change in behavior in his later years was good, at least on an academic level, but in my heart, I was furious with him. He had eighteen years to see the error of his ways and try to make things right with me, and it never happened. Even now, when he had clearly had a change of heart, he didn't apologize to me. He didn't own his mistakes. It felt like he was saying through his actions that my sibling's feelings mattered, his grandchild's feelings mattered, but mine didn't.

But what if he had apologized to me? What would I do with that? Would that undo all the rage and hostility I felt towards him? Could I suddenly release the need for him to suffer and consider the scales of justice balanced? Not likely.

I wiped the tears from my cheeks and took a deep, shaky breath. "I thought I had worked all this out, but I guess I still have some issues with him." My effort at a smile came out more like a grimace.

"That's okay," Nysa said. "That's what we're doing here." She made a few more notes, then turned back to me. "Okay, let's work out your cognitions, and then we'll call it a day. Next week we'll get right into some processing. Sound good?"

"Sure." I felt heavy, as if I were at the bottom of a lake. Most of the things we'd worked on had been processed in a single session, but this definitely wouldn't be. It wasn't surprising. My issues with my dad were at the core of nearly everything in my life. I'd been chipping away layers for a long time, but this was no onion layer. It was ground zero, the epicenter of destruction.

"It sounds like your negative cognition is something like, *I can't accept my dad*," Nysa said. "What do you think?"

"That seems like a good starting point. So I guess my positive would be that I do accept him?"

"Okay. We can always change it if we need to." She closed the folder and set it beside her with a flourish.

I leaned back in my chair. This had been a heavy session, and it was easy to feel like I hadn't made any progress. It was as if I had come into it feeling ambivalent about my dad, and I was leaving with a burning rage. In reality, the rage had been there all along. It had been there for forty years, buried but smoldering, like a vein of burning coal inside a mountain. This was a fire that wasn't going to be extinguished by burying it again. It had to be extracted, ember by ember, and doused with water and intention. It wasn't going to be easy.

Chapter 16

Nysa waved me through the door into her office. "What's up? How was your week?"

I took my spot in the chair and reclined it a bit. How was my week? Terrible. The unfinished business with my dad had been hanging on me since our previous session, and I didn't like that negative feeling. It was too close to the way I used to feel all the time. "It's been a down week," I said. "I've been irritable and moody. I'm ready to finish processing this stuff with my dad."

She grabbed my folder off the desk on her way to the couch and flipped it open. "So last week we talked about how your dad might have accepted you, but you couldn't accept him."

"Right," I said. "I'm pretty sure I've never accepted him. Or my mom, for that matter. I know that acceptance and approval aren't the same thing, like we've talked about before. It's just, I don't know, when I picture him, acceptance is not what I feel at all."

Nysa swung the paddles over to me. "Let's check in on our cognitions. Last week we settled on, *I can't accept my dad* and *I do accept my dad.* Do those still feel right?"

"I think so."

"Okay. One to ten. Paired with your dad dying, how disturbing does it feel to say, *I can't accept my dad*?"

I took a deep breath and let it out. "Ten."

"Paired with your dad's death, how true does it feel to say, *I do accept him*? One to seven."

"Two."

She wrote down my answers. "Okay, let's do some processing. Just go with your thoughts."

The paddles came on, and I settled deeper into the chair and closed my eyes. There were so many occasions when I thought I had finally done something that my dad would be proud of. In my high school ag class, I learned how to arc weld. That was a practical skill, something that my dad would consider useful and important. He didn't place any value on things like English and science, but rather blue-collar skills like auto mechanics, welding, and woodshop. Even then, I knew it was because he didn't understand the more complex things. I could grasp them, but I took the trades classes because I thought that's what he would approve of. I despised him, I spent a huge portion of my time fantasizing about my escape from him, I resented everything about him, and I was still trying to become someone he would approve of, someone he would respect. Someone who was not me.

My big welding project in ag class was a roping dummy. It was a cow constructed out of pipe, with horns and swinging back legs. Cowboys used these to teach their kids how to rope a cow. Mine was far from perfect. The dimensions were all wonky, and it ended up being a lot bigger than it needed to be, but I was proud of it. There were a couple of really good welds on it, in addition to some not-so-good welds, but I wanted my dad to see that I could run a bead with an arc welder. This was my proof to him that I could do something useful.

After months of work I got it home and stood by, waiting as he inspected it.

"The back legs are too far apart," he said.

"I know. I should have cut the crosspiece a little shorter."

He walked to the front end and ran a finger across one of the welds. I held my breath. His finger was just inches away from my two best welds, but it was hovering over my worst weld.

"You burned through the pipe," he grunted. "Rain is going to get in there and rust it out."

I leaned over and pointed to the head. "Did you see these beads? I made it all the way around the joint without losing the pattern."

He glanced at the weld I was pointing to. "Um hmm." He turned and walked toward the house. "Fill up the wood box before supper."

I kicked the roping dummy, disgusted with myself for not fixing the flaws before bringing it home. He was right. A couple of good welds didn't make it a good product. It was a piece of junk with a couple of good welds. What had I been thinking?

The paddles stopped buzzing, bringing me back to the present. My eyes opened slowly, settling on the ceramic snail in front of me.

"What's coming up?"

I chuckled dryly. "I was just thinking about high school. My dad was a blue-collar, hands dirty kind of guy. I was a book smart kid, stage choir, high IQ, all that. And even though I just wanted to get away, I still tried to meet him on his turf. I tried to learn skills that were in his arena, not mine, just so he'd think I was doing something worthwhile."

"And did it work?"

I shook my head. "No, of course not. I wasn't very good at any of those things, for starters. And I didn't take the time to perfect anything before I presented it to him. The lamp I made in woodshop, the roping dummy I made in ag class, all those things. I got excited about what he was going to think, and I rushed them. I took home things with lots of flaws, thinking he was going to be wowed by what I did. I was doing the same thing over and over, expecting different results."

"Okay, let's do it again. Remember your cognitions." She flipped the switch, and the paddles began buzzing in my palms again, left, right, left, right.

I can't accept my dad. My dad was so critical of everything I did. I told myself it was because he wanted me to be better, to always strive for more, but it was a blow to the stomach every time he overlooked a success and pointed out a failure.

I went back to the ranch in Wyoming, to the day I brought the roping dummy home from school. My dad stood there beside it, the usual scowl on his face. His long dark hair was peppered with gray by then, still hanging down his back in two braids. His bushy beard was turning gray too, and I was nearly seven inches taller than him. He had to look up at me, which he usually did over the top of his glasses. It looked like a scowl whether he meant it or not, as it caused his forehead to wrinkle, and that expression is how he looked in nearly all my memories. Brow creased, chin down, glaring at me over the top of his glasses.

His motives were immaterial. Whether he was trying to crush me or raise me up, it didn't matter. The real issue here was whether I could accept him or not. I stared at him, trying to find some measure of empathy or compassion, something to get me a step or two closer to acceptance.

I flashed to another time, back to the house in Oklahoma. My dad spent a few winters trying to make extra money as a trapper. I don't think it was really about the extra money as much as it was about my dad trying to be a mountain man, a hero of the 1700s. He would go check his traps after work and bring home a pile of dead racoons and opossums with the occasional rabbit or skunk. He also trapped beaver, which was the gold doubloon of pelts. He skinned the beavers, as I couldn't be trusted with the high-value hides. My job was to skin everything else.

It was freezing in the garage where this took place. There was a stove in one corner, but if it got too warm, the bodies would start to decay, so there was never a fire in it. My hands would be so cold I could hardly hold on to the butcher knife, and I lived in fear of dropping it and cutting my foot off. I hated the smell of the dead animals. I hated their cold, unblinking eyes staring at me as I hung them upside down on the gamble. I hated that they had to die for some charade my dad was playing. I hated the fact that none of the other kids at school had to do things like this. It made me feel like an outsider, different. Rejected. How was I supposed to accept my dad when he—?

It hit me then, and my eyes flew open.

"I'm trying for the wrong thing!"

Nysa shut the paddles off, a faint smile on her face. "Breakthrough moment?"

"Yes, definitely. I don't need to accept my dad. I never have, and why should I now? I don't need to accept him. I need to *forgive* him." I leaned forward in triumph.

"Yes!" Nysa shouted, leaping off the couch. "You did it! I knew you'd get there." She dropped back down after giving me a high five, and we sat grinning at one another for a moment.

"I'm going to need some help with that," I said, my excitement fading at the prospect of my next task. "As we've learned, I'm still carrying some resentments."

"You can do this," Nysa said. "You made it all the way to Mordor. All you have to do is throw the ring in the fire at Mount Doom."

Her reference to *The Lord of the Rings* made me smile, but it was also a great analogy. I had come too far to quit or to be overcome by self-doubt. And even though I was the only one who could complete the task, I was far from alone. My wonderful wife and my amazing therapist had been there with me every step of the way, and they weren't going to abandon me.

"Okay, how do I do this?" I asked.

"Let's start with some visualization and a new positive cognition. I want you to go back to each of the moments we've talked about with your dad; stacking firewood, digging the ditch, scaring you and making you feel bad for it, sending you out to talk your mom off the suicidal ledge, all of them. Stand beside your younger self, look at your dad, and use this positive cognition: *I can forgive you.* Find the resentment you have for that situation, that negative belief about yourself, and give it back to him. You're done with it now."

"Okay." I leaned back and took a deep breath, letting it out slowly. My shoulders relaxed, followed by my chest, and I did it again. The paddles began buzzing as I let the air trickle out my nose, left, right, left, right.

I went back to 1983, to the woodpile behind the house. My dad stood there with the board, ready to whip me. The rage was there, but it was weak now, and I pushed it away. The time for rage was over. All it did was drain my energy. He was dead; being mad at him did nothing to hurt him.

My new positive cognition felt right. This wasn't about acceptance or approval. What was done was done, and I just wanted to move on. "I don't have to be perfect," I whispered. My voice was weak and shaky, so I cleared my throat and tried again. "I'm good enough, and I don't need to punish myself for not being perfect. I forgive you for making me think that."

I wasn't sure what to expect. There were no fireworks, nothing dramatic. My chest felt empty, lighter, perhaps. Seven-year-old Justin was in my Pensieve now, hanging out with Bilbo Baggins. It was just me and my dad beside the woodpile. He looked small, and not nearly as powerful as I'd always made him out to be. He was just a broken man with a head full of issues that he couldn't deal with. *I forgive you.* I almost felt sorry for him. Almost.

I shifted to the kitchen of the house in Bartlesville back in 1979. My dad stood there, so young then, clean-shaven with short hair, gas mask in hand. His plan had never been to make me feel bad, he just wanted to scare me and have some fun. Yes, it had all gone wrong, and he lost his temper and made a mistake. I conjured up a piece of paper with the word *sissy* written on it in crayon. He stood there in a shaft of sunlight, his hair tousled from the mask and a look of disappointment on his face. I stepped forward and tucked the piece of paper into his shirt pocket. "I'm giving this word back to you. I don't need it anymore. I forgive you."

I took a step back and let the empty feeling come into my chest again. It felt good, clean, like the world after a rainstorm.

Now that I'd done it a few times, I felt a groove forming, and I flashed forward a few years to the ditch digging project in Dewey.

My dad and I stood at one end of the trench. It stretched away to the other end of the house, flanked by the berm of dirt I'd dug out. I turned to face my dad. "This was a huge task, and I did it. I did it, and I did it all by myself. I don't need you to acknowledge that anymore. I know I made a huge contribution, and I've learned how to feel good about myself. Whatever your hang-up was for not being able to tell me I did a good job, I forgive you. I forgive you, and I don't need your validation anymore."

The paddles stopped buzzing, and my eyes flew open. "I'm not done, give me a few more minutes."

Nysa flipped the switch silently, and the paddles resumed. Back at the ditch, I felt a sense of pride. It had been a lot of hard work, and I'd done it. Like the firewood, my only reward had been a whipping for the imperfections. I gazed placidly at my dad, understanding better than ever before how tormented he must have been. I had been a wounded animal in my twenties, and he was no different. *I forgive you.*

I went back a couple of years to Christmas of 1982. The bundle of sticks sat under the tree on one side, in stark contrast to the small pile of presents on the other side despite the bright red ribbon tied around the middle in a bow. My parents sat on the floor in front of the tree, smiling as they took pictures of my baby sister, who was tucked inside a big red stocking.

Empathy was hard in this scene. I tried to find some way of feeling compassion, but there was little for me to draw on. I had a smart mouth as a kid, but I hadn't been *bad.* I wasn't spray-painting graffiti on the school walls or burning down abandoned houses. I wasn't stealing, or lying, or running away. In the realm of kids behaving badly, I wasn't even on the spectrum.

I gave up on empathy. It wasn't necessary for this task, it just made it easier to achieve forgiveness. Stepping around the bundle of sticks, I squatted down in front of my dad so I could look him in the face.

"I've learned that I have value. It took me a long time to get there, but I made it. I know that I matter. I'm not invisible to the people who are important to me. So, I forgive you for making me feel that way. I forgive you for being flawed. I forgive you for taking your pain out on me."

I reached behind me and grabbed the bundle of sticks. The yellow Post-it Note with my name on it was still stuck to a piece of wood. I conjured up a magic marker and crossed my name out and set the bundle on the floor in front of my dad. "I'm giving this back to you. I never deserved it, and I don't need to carry it around anymore."

I stood up, glancing around the room one more time. Hopefully, I would never need to come here again.

The paddles stopped buzzing in my hands, and I opened my eyes to find Nysa looking at me, her eyebrows raised questioningly. "How did it go?"

"Pretty good, really. Better than I thought it would."

"How did it feel to tell your dad you forgive him?"

It was hard to put it into words. "Freeing, in a way. Empowering. Seeing him in those situations, but with the knowledge and perspective I have now, really changed the power dynamic. I even had empathy for him a few times. It felt good to give him back the negative ideas of myself that he gave me. That was pretty awesome. That reminds me, I wanted to show you something."

She smiled uncertainly as she waited for me to continue.

"I've been playing with design ideas for the book cover, and I hit on one that I like." I pulled my phone out and showed her a picture. "I thought that putting a bundle of sticks on the cover would be pretty symbolic of things, with the Christmas bow."

"Ooh, I love it!" A smile split her face. "You made this?"

I nodded. "It's just a concept cover for my designer to work from. But anyway, that's not the thing. I couldn't find a picture online that I liked, so I decided to make my own. I walked around the yard and picked up all these sticks and tied a ribbon around them. While I was doing that, it occurred to me that I was doing the exact same thing my dad did way back when. It was a meta moment. But what hit me is that I still have the bundle of sticks from the picture, and I can do a little forgiveness ceremony and burn them. I already gave them back to my dad just now, but burning them would be even more symbolic since he's dead. Ashes and smoke, letting it all go back to the universe."

Nysa was nodding as I talked, a smile on her face. "That's a terrific idea. Ceremonies like that are really helpful to a lot of people. Whether it's writing letters, or burning something, or whatever, the process of doing something symbolic like that is a very therapeutic action. You can write a resentment on each of the sticks if you want to, or do whatever feels right to really finalize your forgiveness of your dad. As it burns, you just let it all go."

I hadn't planned for the bundle of sticks to be anything other than a picture for the book cover. Suddenly, it was so much more than that. It was an artifact, a physical manifestation of my childhood pain that I could use to heal myself. It seemed beyond serendipitous that a random thought could turn into something so powerful, as if the universe itself was trying to help me get over this hurdle in my life. The idea was empowering.

I felt clean and empty, as if I had somehow purged all the negative thoughts about myself from my brain. It felt good to feel good, and I tried to focus on the sensation and treasure it while it lasted. It struck me as funny the way I could effortlessly hold on to the bad things, but I had to work at remembering the good things. But if I'd learned anything, it was that I could retrain my brain. I just had to be willing to put in the effort.

Chapter 17

It was a beautiful Sunday afternoon in late October. The temperature was in the low eighties, still warm, but a welcome relief after the heat of the Florida summer. I walked around one of the front pastures gathering fallen limbs, stacking them near the burn pit. The dogs followed me, taking pleasure in the myriad of smells to investigate in the rotting leaves beneath the trees.

I built a medium-sized pyre. It was a combination of dry pine, which would burn hot and fast, and water oak, which was slower to take off but would last a while. Instead of the usual heap of branches, I made this one more of a square. This was going to be a special fire.

When it was ready, I walked back up to the barn. Erica had finished riding and was washing her horse when I arrived.

"I'm ready when you are," I said.

"Give me just a second, I'm almost done here."

"No worries. I'm going to grab the bundle, and I'll meet you out there."

With the dogs on my heels, I walked across the driveway to the covered parking area where we kept the truck and horse trailer. I'd used the concrete driveway there as a backdrop to photograph the bundle of sticks for the book cover, and when I was done, I'd left it sitting against the wall.

The bundle of sticks had only been there for a week, and I wasn't expecting anything to be amiss as I rounded the corner. After all, it was just a few dead branches, nothing that anyone would be interested in. I was surprised to see that some of the sticks were broken in half and had clearly been chewed on. Bits of wood and bark littered the floor around them, and nearby were several piles of poop, identifying the culprits: the sheep.

In a way, it was fitting. My mom and dad would both get a great laugh out of it, and that was an important part of this whole experience. It was about me, yes, but it was about them, too. I chuckled as I gathered up the bundle and the loose pieces that were scattered around it. The ribbon was intact, and I tucked the whole thing under my arm and headed back to the burn pit.

This was supposed to be a soul-cleansing ceremony, which seemed like something I should feel somber about, but it was hard not to smile as the dogs ran around the pasture chasing butterflies. Joy was a big part of my life now, so I stopped worrying about being serious and just enjoyed myself. I placed the sheep-chomped bundle of sticks on top of the pyre and stepped back, waiting for Erica.

When she arrived, I pointed to the stack of wood with a grin. "The sheep tried to eat my bundle of sticks."

Erica laughed. "That sounds exactly like something they would do!"

"I thought it was appropriate." I pulled the lighter out of my pocket. "Ready?"

She nodded. Along with providing moral support, she would take some pictures of the moment for me. I didn't know what I was going to experience, but I wanted to do my best with the ceremony.

I knelt and struck the lighter to the paper at the base of the pyre. Nothing happened. I shook the lighter and confirmed that it still had fluid in it. It was over half full, and there was a good spark, but it wouldn't light.

"This moment symbolizes every task I ever tried to do for my dad," I said with a laugh. "Totally appropriate!"

Erica laughed with me and lowered the phone. "Do you have another lighter?"

"I do, up in the toolbox. I'll be right back."

I jogged back to the barn and returned with the other lighter.

"Okay, let's try this again."

The paper lit on the first strike, and within minutes, the pyre was blazing. I stood back beside Erica, and she grabbed my hand.

"Are you okay?" she asked.

I nodded. It almost seemed like I was doing this wrong, because I didn't feel sad, morose, or any of the things I'd been prepared to feel. To the contrary, I felt whole. Healthy. Instead of crying, which I'd considered a real possibility, I felt like laughing and running around like a little kid. Free.

Erica took a few pictures as the flames climbed. It took a few minutes for them to reach the bundle of sticks on top, but by the time they did, the fire was beginning to burn with intensity. The air above it shimmered from the heat boiling into the sky, and the red ribbon vanished in a curl of black smoke.

I tried to visualize the release of all my resentments against my dad like I had that day in therapy. It seemed fitting that I would send them into the sky with the smoke and ashes caught in the updraft. The problem was that I couldn't find anything to let go of. Maybe it was the beautiful day, or the dogs playing, or my awareness of Erica standing beside me, holding my hand. Across the pasture, the neighbor's goats were bleating in such a pathetic way that I couldn't stop laughing at them, and maybe that was a distraction. Or maybe I really *had* managed to let go of everything already, and this was a celebration of my achievement.

The wind shifted, bringing the heat and smoke over us, and we moved around the fire to get away from it. The ribbon was long gone, but I could still see some of the larger sticks from the bundle at the top of the pyre. They were gray and ashy, with bright orange flames curling around the edges. The pyre was beginning to collapse, and I found my mind and eyes wandering.

Erica gave my hand a squeeze, her eyes searching my face. I'd prepared her for the worst so that she wouldn't worry if I stood here and bawled my eyes out, and I was almost embarrassed that I was handling it so well. I smiled at her as I squeezed her hand back.

"I guess I'm done grieving about it," I said with a slight shrug.

"That's good," she said. "Did you do what you wanted to do?"

"I think so. I did what I needed to do, anyway. I thought there might be more drama to it, but maybe not. I spent more time enjoying the dogs and the goats than anything."

A hawk sailed overhead, momentarily blocking the sun. I took one last look at the fire, searching for any last urges to complete the ceremony. The bundle of sticks was gone, and the pyre had collapsed into a bed of glowing coals. I felt good about myself, and I knew I'd accomplished something important. It feels good to feel good, as the saying goes. Having spent a lifetime feeling bad about myself, I relished this contrasting perspective. I hoped it would be a long time before the novelty wore off.

We turned our backs to the fire and walked slowly across the pasture toward the house. Despite the season, I noticed some small blue flowers in the late summer grass. The world was alive. I was alive. And I was better than I'd ever been. It was exhilarating to know that my best days were still in front of me, and there was hope on the horizon.

Afterword

I FINISHED WRITING the rough draft of this book in November 2020, a year that will not be forgotten anytime soon. I sent it off to my editor, and while she was working on it, I decided to let my mom know that I'd written it. In our world of internet and social media, she was bound to find out that it existed, and it seemed prudent to tell her ahead of time.

Being my mother, she went through an emotional ride full of ups and downs, first going to one extreme and then another. She felt horrible, thinking about how her actions had hurt me, and she was embarrassed that I wanted to tell the whole world. I shared the first few chapters with her, and as our emails continued, she began to see how she'd been just as much a victim of her upbringing as I had. She even began to see how others who suffer from self-image issues might learn from this book and seek their own help. And finally, just before Christmas 2020, she decided that after the holidays were done, she was going to begin therapy. Finally.

And then she died.

On January 1st, 2021, my mother died from COVID-19. To go back to my driftwood analogy, she finally asked me to throw her a life ring, but before she could grab it, a wave took her under, and she never came back up.

So, yeah, I'm back in therapy.

I'm so grateful that I already had a relationship with my therapist. It made getting an emergency appointment much easier, and we were able to get right to the point and process the end of my mom's life. If ever there was a time for me to have an emotional guide, that was it. I'm also grateful to be sober. That allowed me to handle things much better than I did when my dad died.

Writing this book was almost as healing as the therapy I went though. It's helped me solidify the things I've learned about myself and really round out the image of who I actually am. Learning that just about everything I ever believed about myself was wrong left me with a sense of being lost, unsure of my place in the world. I've spent the last ten years trying to build a new foundation. It wasn't easy, but it was definitely worthwhile.

While I wrote this book for me, I decided to share it with you for several reasons. It's no secret that the world is filled with emotionally damaged people. I can't speak for anyone else, but I knew something was wrong with me most of my life. The problem was that I didn't know what to do about it. I had serious hang-ups in my younger years about asking for help. The ridiculous idea that a man, a real man, is tough and doesn't ask anyone for anything kept me from even considering therapy for a very long time. I didn't feel like a real tough guy, but I thought I was supposed to keep that image going so no one would think I was weak or broken.

At this point in my life, I have a very different idea about manliness and strength and what's important. The idea of putting on a façade to impress someone else seems crazy and even sad to me now, especially if it makes me miserable. If I can't feel good about who I am while I'm doing something, then I need to look at what I'm doing. Being true to myself and taking care of my needs are far more important than managing someone else's opinion of me.

When I'm ninety and looking back over my life, I'm not going to be proud of my ability to take a beating while not showing any pain. I'm not going to measure my life by how tough I was, or how unwilling I was to let anyone teach me something. And I'm not going to put much stock in the opinions of people who use those things to measure a person's value. They might be important on the elementary school playground, but they're pretty destructive concepts for an adult to live by.

No, today, being a real man means being honest about what's going on inside, and fixing things that need fixing. It's about knowing who I am, and who I'm trying to become. It's about being committed to growth and self-improvement, and not compromising my values. It's about recognizing when I need help with something and seeking out that help.

I said all that to say this: there's no reason to be miserable. If you need help, it's out there. As a wise person once said: Pain is inevitable, but suffering is optional. I found my way out of the darkness, and I hope you do, too.

Justin B. Long
February 2021

P.S. If you got something from this book, please consider giving it a review wherever you purchased it! That's a great way to help others decide if it's a good book for them to try. And I know I'm not supposed to need outside validation, and maybe someday I won't, but I'd be lying if I said I didn't love seeing what people thought of my books. I've been through a lot of therapy, but I'm not done yet!

Justin B. Long is a self-embracing nerd who loves crunching numbers, researching interesting things, and listening to podcasts, in addition to reading loads of books. By day he is the CFO of Springhill Equine Veterinary Clinic, and by night he is a science fiction and memoir author. When he's not responding to after-hours horse emergencies or dreaming up alternate dimensions of reality, he enjoys hiking in national parks. He lives near Gainesville, Florida on a small farm with his incredible wife, 7 horses, 5 cats, 2 donkeys, 2 dogs, and a sheep named Gerald. Find out more at JBoydLong.com.

Made in the USA
Las Vegas, NV
04 April 2023